A SUSSEX KIPLING

Selected & annotated
by David Arscott

Published by Pomegranate Press,
Dolphin House, 51 St Nicholas Lane, Lewes, Sussex BN7 2JZ
pomegranatepress@aol.com
www.pomegranate-press.co.uk

ISBN: 978–0–954–89751–2

Photographs by David Arscott
Illustrations by David Marl, except those on pages 15, 27, 86 and 136 by Peter
Berrisford

Permission to use extracts from *Something of Myself* and from Kipling's letters granted
by A.P. Watt Ltd on behalf of The National Trust for Places of Historic Interest or
Natural Beauty

British Library Cataloguing-in-Publication Data.
A catalogue record for this book is available from the British Library

Printed and bound by 4Edge, 7A Eldon Way, Hockley, Essex SS5 4AD

CONTENTS

Kipling called the stone path flanking Bateman's the Quarter Deck, and it was while pacing up and down it that he planned many of his poems and stories.

INTRODUCTION

Rudyard Kipling was a much-travelled man, but to only two parts of the world did he commit both his heart and his pen. The first of these was India, the land of his infancy and of his early manhood. The second was Sussex, the land of his maturity.

When he moved to the county with his young family in 1897 he was already famous for his Indian stories and verses, and was soon to be infamous for his increasingly strident views on Britain's imperial role in dangerous times. If those aspects of his life and work still largely define Kipling in the popular imagination, Sussex was to stimulate his passionate curiosity for the best part of 40 years and, as these pages reveal, was to inspire some of his finest writing.

The young Kipling in his India days.

His earlier years need only be sketched in here. Born in Bombay in 1865, he was brought up among house servants whose Hindustani dialect he was inclined to speak rather than the English of his middle-class family. He was brutally wrenched from this colourful Raj milieu at the age of five, dispatched with his younger sister Alice (known as Trix, and then but rising three) to the care of strangers in Southsea, near Portsmouth. After several miserable years in what he was later to call The House of Desolation, he was enrolled at the newly formed United Services College in Devon (which gave him the material for the schoolboy stories in *Stalky & Co*) before, a little short of his 17th birthday, he returned to India to become a journalist on *The Civil and Military Gazette* in Lahore.

This was in late 1882. By the time that he was promoted to the paper's sister publication, the *Pioneer,* in Allahabad five years later he had thoroughly immersed himself in both native and colonial life, had published *Departmental Ditties* to great acclaim and was about to enjoy a similar success with *Plain Tales from the Hills*. He returned to England in 1889 at the age of twenty-three, already a celebrated author on both sides of the Atlantic, and would pay only one brief further visit to India during the rest of his life.

In 1892 he married Caroline Balestier, an American with whose brother, Wolcott, he had enjoyed a brief but intense friendship before the young man's death from typhoid. For a few years they lived close to her family in Vermont, where their daughters Josephine and Elsie were born, but a badly-handled dispute with Caroline's brother Beatty made it impossible for the Kiplings to remain there. They returned to England, first to Devon and then, within a year, to the village of Rottingdean, near Brighton – which is where this anthology begins.

Although its entries follow a broad chronological sweep, I have allowed myself licence to tinker with the order to suit the book's five sections. The first of these deals with the years at Rottingdean (1897–1902); the second with Kipling's pioneering attachment to the first motor cars; the third with the early period at Bateman's (from 1902 until the first world war); the fourth with his two volumes of children's history stories, *Puck of Pook's Hill* and *Rewards and Fairies*; and the fifth (which touches on the later years at Bateman's) with the strain of mysticism that informs his writing about the Sussex landscape and the people who have possessed it over the centuries.

Those of us who share his love of the territory owe him an inestimable debt of gratitude. Sussex has had more than its fair share of chroniclers and versifiers, but Kipling is the one writer of major stature to have memorialised it with his peculiar genius.

David Arscott
Lewes, 2007

LIFE AT THE ELMS

The writers and artists who congregated around the green in Rottingdean during the last years of the nineteenth century must have seemed an exotic breed to the locals. Bob Copper, in his book *Early to Rise*, recalls that during his childhood a generation later the village still slumbered in a timeless way: 'Sons followed their father's trade or calling without question, for it was considered to be the natural order of things and there still existed a long line of continuity in the patterns of living and established habits in thought, word and deed. With fishermen on the foreshore casting their nets by hand, shepherds watching their flocks on the hillside and sowers flinging their seed to the rhythm of their stride, scenes of Biblical simplicity were part of everyday life.'

Since Kipling was a devoted son, husband and father, it's fitting that it was family ties that brought him to Sussex in the summer of 1897. His mother's sister Georgiana (Aunt Georgie) and her husband, the artist Sir Edward Burne-Jones (Uncle Ned), had opened their house in London to the young Rudyard during the Christmas holidays while he was an unhappy young lad at Southsea – it was, he wrote later, 'a paradise which I verily believe saved me'. North End House in Rottingdean was their summer retreat, and they offered it to the Kiplings when they were expecting their third child, John.

There was a further family connection. On another side of the green lay The Dene, the home of the local squires, the Ridsdales. Kipling's cousin, the future prime minister Stanley Baldwin, (the son of his Aunt Louisa) had married the oldest daughter of the house, Lucy. When a third neighbouring house became available for renting soon afterwards, the Kiplings leapt at the chance and were soon installed at The Elms. Although they were based here until 1902, however, they were away for long stretches at a time. During 1898 they spent four months in South Africa; in 1899 they paid their last visit to the United States; and every year from 1900 until 1908 South Africa drew them again during the winter months.

These years were productive for Kipling, with the completion of *Stalky & Co*, his teeming Indian novel *Kim* and the *Just So Stories*, and they also saw a growing engagement with political issues, especially once the Boer War broke out in 1899. He reported from the battlefields, visited the wounded and wrote his poem *The Absent-Minded Beggar* which, set to music by Sir Arthur Sullivan, raised the then massive sum of £250,000 for soldiers' families. With the onset of peace in 1902, however, Kipling opposed the deal which gave the Boers equal rights in the new Union of South Africa, and thereafter he was to be aggressively at odds with the British government.

His favourite Aunt Georgie took a different view of the war, and greeted the peace by hanging from the window of North End House a black banner inscribed with the message 'We have killed and also taken possession.' A hostile crowd assembled outside, until Kipling managed to persuade them to leave – with mixed feelings, one imagines. His view was that the country was sleep-walking to disaster, ill-prepared for troubles to come.

A disaster of a personal nature had already brought the Kiplings low. Within two years of John's birth they lost six-year-old Josephine to pneumonia. The family had crossed the Atlantic to New York in rough winter seas, and Kipling himself fell dangerously ill, the world daily expecting news of his death. The funeral service took place before he had recovered, and his younger daughter Elsie later wrote that 'a light had gone out that could never be rekindled'.

In his poem 'Merrow Down', included with the *Just So Stories*, Josephine appears in the guise of Taffy, who comes dancing to bring in the spring, 'and lights her little damp-wood smoke/To show her Daddy where she flits'. Kipling himself is the ancient Briton Tegumai, in a final stanza whose tripping rhythms serve only to throw his despair into starker relief:

> For far – oh, very far behind,
>   So far she cannot call to him,
> Comes Tegumai alone to find
>   The daughter that was all to him!

A Child is Born

Letter to Lockwood de Forest, August 17, 1897
It's a sleepy frowzy-headed chap that writes for he has been more or less up all night assisting at a circus. It's a boy – a black haired boy who howls like a month-old baby and, what is of much more importance, Carrie is doing splendidly. Has an even pulse and a good colour and is sleeping. Nothing could be better say the doctor and the nurse: but I shall believe 'em when the next three days are done.

Letter to W.J. Harding [whose guest Kipling had recently been on fleet trials]
My attention is at present taken up by small craft recently launched from my own works – weight (approx) 8.957 lbs: h.p (indicated) 2.0464, consumption of fuel unrecorded but fresh supplies needed every $2\frac{1}{2}$ hrs. The vessel at present needs at least 15 years for full completion but at the end of that time may be an efficient addition to the Navy, for which service it is intended. Date of launch Aug. 17th 1.50 a.m. No casualties. Christened John. You will understand that the new craft requires a certain amount of attention – but I trust ere long to be able to attend a t.b.d. [torpedo boat destroyer] trial.

The Elms at Rottingdean today – fittingly with a Rolls-Royce sitting outside.

From 'Something of Myself'

Our flight from Torquay ended almost by instinct at Rottingdean where the beloved Aunt and Uncle had their holiday house, and where I had spent my very last days before sailing for India fourteen years back. In 1882 there had been but one daily bus from Brighton, which took forty minutes; and when a stranger appeared on the village green the native young would stick out their tongues at him. The Downs poured almost direct into the one village street and lay out eastward unbroken to Russia Hill above Newhaven. It was little altered in '96. My cousin, Stanley Baldwin, had married the eldest daughter of the Ridsdales out of The Dene – the big house that flanked one side of the green. My Uncle's North End House commanded the other, and a third house opposite the church was waiting to be taken according to the decrees of Fate. The Baldwin marriage, then, made us free of the joyous young brotherhood and sisterhood of The Dene, and its friends.

The Aunt and Uncle had said to us: 'Let the child that is coming to you be born in our house,' and had effaced themselves till my son John arrived on a warm August night of '97, under what seemed every good omen.

Letter to Sara Norton, August 21, 1897

Yours is the fine round rolling handwriting that can be read in sick-rooms without difficulty and Carrie shall be cheered with it after breakfast. Yes,

The Dene, formerly the home of the Ridsdale family.

she is coming on all right – better in fact than I've ever known her to do before and is just now starting the campaign of nursing John. Reserved young person John: but considerably better looking than he was two days ago. He lacks ideality but he has his mother's mouth, is a short square baby with a thick set look about him.

I am studying the English from an entirely new point of view – the doctor and the nurse being the glasses. They are amazing. C. is naturally languorous and does not demand novels or a skirt-dance on the third or fourth day – and they don't understand it. She is 'an 'ealthy little lady' says the nurse. 'Why don't she pick up like the others?' Rummy! But when you come to think of it they can't make any special fuss about birth in this land and 'shock' they have heard of but do not understand. She is healthy – why should she feel it at all? I have explained that one of the many inexplicable peculiarities of the American woman is to feel that kind of thing: and that they the doctor and the nurse must allow for it. They are both very good and kind, and the nurse is splendid in her nursing.

The doctor is only coming every other day now and C. is being stuffed with food. Mrs Shergold keeps a wary eye on her and cooks, I think, all the time. She is thoroughly enjoying herself and grieves audibly when C. doesn't demand a new dish every two hours . . .

Carrie joins me in every good wish (she's an 'ealthy little lady. Why do she notice it so?)

From 'Something of Myself'
Meantime, we had rented by direct interposition of Fate that third house opposite the church on the green. It stood in a sort of little island behind flint walls which we then thought were high enough, and almost beneath some big ilex trees. It was small, none too well built, but cheap . . . Then there grew up great happiness between The Dene, North End House and The Elms. One could throw a cricket-ball from any one house to the other, but, beyond turning out at 2 a.m. to help a silly fox-hound puppy who had stuck in a drain, I do not remember any violent alarms and excursions other than packing farm-carts with mixed babies – Stanley Baldwin's and ours – and despatching them into the safe clean heart of the motherly Downs for jam-smeared picnics. Those Downs moved me to write some verses called 'Sussex'. Today, from Rottingdean to Newhaven is almost fully developed suburb, of great horror.

The surprising thing about Kipling's hymn to his adopted county is that it was written so soon after his settling here – in 1902. By then, of course, he had begun the motoring journeys which feature in the next section and, an ardent as well as a keenly observant traveller, he had no doubt already immersed himself in the available historical and topographical works. Sussex was, he wrote to a friend, 'the most marvellous of all foreign countries that I have ever been in.'

God gave all men all earth to love,
  But, since our hearts are small,
Ordained for each one spot should prove
  Belovèd over all;
That, as He watched Creation's birth,
  So we, in godlike mood,
May of our love create our earth
  And see that it is good.

So one shall Baltic pines content,
  As one some Surrey glade,

Strip lynchets on the Downs.

12

Or one the palm-grove's droned lament
  Before Levuka's Trade.
Each to his choice, and I rejoice
  The lot has fallen to me
In a fair ground – in a fair ground –
  Yea, Sussex by the sea!

No tender-hearted garden crowns,
  No bosomed woods adorn
Our blunt, bow-headed, whale-backed Downs,
  But gnarled and writhen thorn –
Bare slopes where chasing shadows skim,
  And through the gaps revealed,
Belt upon belt, the wooded, dim,
  Blue goodness of the Weald.

Clean of officious fence or hedge,
  Half-wild and wholly tame,
The wise turf cloaks the white cliff-edge
  As when the Romans came.
What sign of those that fought and died
  At shift of sword and sword?
The barrow and the camp abide,
  The sunlight and the sward.

Here leaps ashore the full Sou'west
  All heavy-winged with brine,
Here lies above the folded crest
  The channel's leaden line;
And here the sea-fogs lap and cling,
  And here, each warning each,
The sheep-bells and the ship-bells ring
  Along the hidden beach.

We have no waters to delight
  Our broad and brookless vales –
Only the dewpond on the height
  Unfed, that never fails –
Whereby no tattered herbage tells
  Which way the season flies –
Only our close-bit thyme that smells
  Like dawn in Paradise.

Here through the strong and shadeless days
  The tinkling silence thrills;
Or little, lost, Down churches praise
  The Lord who made the hills:
But here the Old Gods guard their round,
  And in her secret heart,
The heathen kingdom Wilfrid found
  Dreams, as she dwells, apart.

Though all the rest were all my share,
  With equal soul I'd see
Her nine-and-thirty sister fair,
  Yet none more fair than she.
Choose ye your need from Thames to Tweed,
  And I will choose instead
Such lands as lie 'twixt Rake and Rye,
  Black Down and Beachy Head.

I will go out against the sun
  Where the rollèd scarp retires,
And the Long Man of Wilmington
  Looks naked toward the shires;
And east till doubling Rother crawls
  To find the fickle tide,
By dry and sea-forgotten walls,
  Our ports of stranded pride.

*One of Kipling's 'little,
lost, Down churches' –
Lullington in East Sussex*

14

*'Dry and sea-forgotten walls':
the Strand Gate at Winchelsea.
Like those at Rye, Seaford and
Bramber, the town's harbour
became badly silted when the
sea retreated in medieval times,
so ruining trade.*

I will go north about the shaws
  And the deep ghylls that breed
Huge oaks and old, the which we hold
  No more than Sussex weed;
Or south where windy Piddinghoe's
  Begilded dolphin veers,
And red beside wide-bankèd Ouse
  Lie down our Sussex steers.

So to the land our hearts we give
  Till the sure magic strike,
And Memory, Use and Love make live
  Us and our field alike –
That deeper than our speech and thought,
  Beyond our reason's sway,
Clay of the pit whence we were wrought
  Yearns to its fellow-clay.

*God gives all men all earth to love,
  But, since man's heart is small,
Ordains for each one spot shall prove
  Belovèd over all.
Each to his choice, and I rejoice
  The lot has fallen to me
In a fair ground – in a fair ground –
  Yea, Sussex by the sea!*

Meet the Committee

The short autobiographical extract which follows contains a mention in short form of what Kipling generally called The Committee of Ways and Means. Originally (as here) referring in jocular terms to the domestic arrangements practised by husband and wife together, it comes to be used more in the singular as Carrie – a formidable house-keeper – takes an iron grip on the family purse and appointments diary.

From 'Something of Myself'

When the Burne-Jones' returned to their own North End House, all was more than well. My Uncle's world was naturally not mine, but his heart and brain were large enough to take in any universe, and in the matter of doing one's own work in one's own way he had no doubts. His golden laugh, his delight in small things and the perpetual war of practical jokes that waged between us, was refreshment after working hours. And when we cousins, Phil, his son, Stanley Baldwin and I, went to the beach and came back with descriptions of fat bathers, he would draw them,

The Burne-Jones home. The family bought the house on the left (then Prospect Cottage) in 1880, soon afterwards adding the property in the middle (Aubrey Cottage) and renaming the expanded building North End House. In 1923 Gothic House on the right was acquired to create an imposing three-in-one pile.

indescribably swag-bellied, wallowing in the surf. Those were exceedingly good days, and one's work came easily and fully . . .

At The Elms, Rottingdean, the sou'-wester raged day and night, till the silly windows jiggled their wedges loose. (Which was why the Committee vowed never to have a house of their own with up-and-down windows. *Cf.* Charles Reade on that subject.) But I was quite unconcerned . . . At last I reported *Kim* finished. 'Did it stop, or you?' the Father asked. And when I told him that it was It, he said: 'Then it oughtn't to be too bad.'

A ROTTINGDEAN FUNERAL

Sir Edward Burne-Jones died at his home in Fulham on June 16, 1898, was cremated at Woking and was laid to rest in the churchyard at Rottingdean. Kipling's long letter to the American critic Charles Eliot Norton (abbreviated here) gives a vivid picture of mourning in the village. It also, in passing but twice over, touches on Kipling's view of art and writing as a workman's job rather than a dilletante's pastime.

Letter to Charles Eliot Norton, June 1898

It came, of course, most utterly unexpectedly – and the first news, on Thursday morning last, was a telegram from Phil to the vicar here saying that his father had died that same morning. Even so, the thing seemed like some sort of ghastly hoax because we had been in correspondence with Aunt Georgie on small matters day by day and her last letter said that she was coming down with Ned in a few days. Then, at midday, of Friday, came a letter – one of his wild, nonsensical 'lark' letters – to me: a beautiful tissue of absurdities. He said he was a bit fagged working at the Avalon picture, standing up all day and dozing in the evening when he wasn't dining out. That was posted about an hour before he died. As you know it was heart-failure of some sort or other. They called it *angina-pectoris* and it may have been so: but when a man has worked without rest for forty years, the failure may take any shape. It was clean, clear overwork – as good a death on the field as ever man could desire. They two by good luck had their last evening alone. They dined alone, and talked and read together alone, and Ned was very happy. Then he went to bed, and about two o'clock called up Georgie with some word that he had a bad touch of heartburn. Before half-past two – before any one of his blood could come – he died in Aunt Georgie's arms and that was as it should be (I fancy he had complained of some uneasiness that afternoon: and his doctor looked him over and told him that there was nothing wrong with his heart). The mercy of it was unspeakable – when you think of all that vile crowded London life so near to them. He might have been struck down in public – at a theatre or dining out somewhere; instead of in his own place, quietly and shieldedly. And so he died – Avalon unfinished: and of course, a mass of other unfinished work waiting. There wasn't anything to be done at our end of the calamity but to wait – to sit still and wait and see what would happen. He was more to me than any man here: over and above my own life's love for him: and he had changed my life in many ways by his visits down here. The man was a God to me – as a workman I can't tell you about that side of it and it doesn't very much matter now.

Sallie knows the Rottingdean church where Margot [Burne-Jones's daughter] was married and where his seven windows are. Last autumn he went for a walk and caught the vicar – who is a good man but I should fancy a bit bewildered by Uncle Ned, who wanted, so he said, a 'cozy place' for his ashes. The spot he chose was roughly where I have marked in the sketch here – a little recess facing to North End House, in the arm, so to speak, of the S.W. buttress of the church – a place shut out from all the winds, and surrounded with a high border of valerian – purple and white spikes. It is rising ground and, as I said, he can look straight across the green, a bare fifty yards, to the windows of North End House. He told us of the place, on the evening of the day of that walk, and explained – you know how he would – its advantages. There, then, the grave was made but, thank Heaven, it wasn't any yawning pit because he had left orders to be cremated.

The little box of ashes was laid in front of the altar on his drawing table – no drapery, no nonsense – no nothing except four candles and there it was

Rottingdean church, south-west buttress.

18

watching through the night – the night of midsummer eve – a hot, still grey night with no true darkness at all: but our northern twilight. Phil and Jack Mackail stayed from eight till twelve; then a friend of theirs, Harry Taylor, from twelve to two; Stan from two to four; I from four to six; and Uncle Alfred from six to eight. In Stan's watch just as the true dawn was breaking Aunt Georgie and Margot came in, all in white, to watch a little and dear old Stan said he felt like a profane heathen and crept out till they called him back. I can believe it for her face in daylight was like nothing earthly. In my watch there came in the old, old Mr Ridsdale, father of Stan's wife, Cissy – rather an appalling figure at five a.m. – scrupulously dressed in black; looking rather like Father Time strayed in from among the tombs; and he stayed an hour. It was an unearthly night but for the life of me I could not connect the man who was three parts a God with the little oak box before me. The drawing table and the windows were much more him.

St Margaret window
by Burne-Jones.

Tuesday was one long nightmare of which I don't remember much. People wandered about doing things in an aimless purposeless way. There was a good deal to be done, I know, and I tried to do some things but it was all no good. One couldn't stay to anything. Father came down from London (Mother and Aunt Edie stayed together at Tisbury) and with him came Aunt Aggie, Uncle Edward, Ambo – Fred Macdonald with two sons, and we all herded together in the Elms. There were a lot of other people in the churchyard and on the green but I can't say I took an extravagant interest in them. The simplicity and quiet of the arrangements had cut down all outsiders to the smallest number: but from my point of view one didn't need any more. At two the English burial service began in the church and Aunt Georgie was there with all the others. Then Phil and Margot themselves carried the box to the grave which was lined with moss and roses and themselves let it down at the last – so that no hands, except those of his own blood, touched him. The decency, the cleanliness and the sanity of it all were as he would have wished. I had had a horror in my mind of some bungling, hireling business with ropes and boards. All that thank God was done away with.

That same evening Aunt Georgie and the others went up to town again. We saw the grave (only it wasn't a grave, thank God) put in order:

with some flowers from Ruskin and a wreath from Swinburne – no dirt on the edges: no mess – nothing but decency and order. Our gardener who has seen Uncle Ned of course from afar, said to me reflectively: 'Of course I hadn't anything to do with him: but what did strike me about him' (I use the man's own words) 'was his humanity. There aren't many too humane men in the world today – are they?' That struck me as very curious. You see in point of space we are nearer to Uncle Ned even than North End House, because he is only just across the road and, being a dry season, Marten the gardener waters the grass on his own initiative for the sake of the 'humane man'. The village kept itself quite quiet. The regular omnibus which blows a disgusting horn round the green, kept away and (I know something about the common folk here) everyone was sorry – really sorry for the loss. They knew in their several ways that he was the 'humane man'. Yesterday (Wednesday) was the memorial service in the Abbey to which Carrie and I went, but I should not have gone if I had realised that all the English church could do in the way of a memorial would be to repeat practically the whole of the burial for the dead. There was fine music and a choir, a Dean in black and white and red (a little shrivelled figure against the background of gold) but I kept seeing the Rottingdean of the day before under my eyelids all the time.

I can't cry. At least I don't seem able to have found out the way yet and I don't think it will come either. It's all a sort of a clot in my head because one has to realise that the man won't come back. Anybody's grief is selfish in essence, of course; and mine probably more selfish than others because I am a selfish man. His work was the least part of him. It is him that one wants – the size and the strength and the power and the jests and the God given sympathy of the man. He knew. There never was man like to him who knew all things without stirring. Last autumn, he was good enough to talk to me after work – and he talked to me like an equal – as though I were also a workman. He could work more and harder and more sustainedly than a navvy – and it was that among a million things that I reverenced him for beside all my love for him. He was never at fault in his discernings: he made all allowances, just as a God would do; and he laughed like a God. You know, things had rather

Weather-worn memorial plaque on the south-west wall of the church.

broken me up before I left America and this thing has snapped something else inside me. It's all in the day's work of course and one must hold on to the end of the day but sometimes one gets a wee bit tired. That's my grief and by the side of the others' it's a little one.

This reconstruction of Kipling's study at The Elms can be seen in the museum at The Grange, Rottingdean.

He insisted on using hand-dipped Waverley pens with the blackest ink he could find, and all his life he wrote on large off-white blue sheets.

MILITARY MATTERS

With the Boer War in full swing, Kipling decided to put his concerns about Britain's other-worldliness into practice. Never mind the insouciance of 'the flannelled fools at the wicket or the muddied oafs at the goals', he would have young men trained for future conflict. They met at a tin drill-shed ten minutes' walk from the village.

His poem 'Recessional' has no local resonance, but it was written at Rottingdean – begun the morning after Queen Victoria's diamond jubilee celebrations and printed in the 'Times'. (George Orwell later suggested that 'lesser breeds without the Law' referred to the despised Germans.) Kipling had no faith, and the religiosity of the lines, although it chimed with the popular sentiment of the day, has something of a worked-up feel about it.

Letter to Julian Ralph, October 15, 1900

Do you want fun and larx? If so, come down on Saturday and help us open the new Rifle Range. It's the end of a year's laborious committee meeting, and untold silly correspondence, and I believe it's the first 1,000 yd range started by purely private enterprise in Gt Britain – we hope to get a real live M.P. to make speeches: we fall in about 40 of us, opposite the Infant School at 2.15 on Saturday afternoon and march down to the butts (you know 'em) and then the wife of the local squire will fire the first shot from a tripod. It will probably rain like blazes but anyhow it will be a deliciously English function and one which you should not miss.

God of our fathers, known of old,
  Lord of our far-flung battle-line,
Beneath whose awful Hand we hold
  Dominion over palm and pine –
Lord God of Hosts, be with us yet,
  Lest we forget – lest we forget!

The tumult and the shouting dies;
  The Captains and the Kings depart:
Still stands Thine ancient sacrifice,
  An humble and a contrite heart.
Lord God of Hosts, be with us yet,
Lest we forget – lest we forget!

Far-called, our navies melt away;
  On dune and headland sinks the fire:
Lo, all our pomp of yesterday
  Is one with Nineveh and Tyre!
Judge of the Nations, spare us yet,
Lest we forget – lest we forget!

If, drunk with sight of power, we loose
  Wild tongues that have not Thee in awe,
Such boastings as the Gentiles use,
  Or lesser breeds without the Law –
Lord God of Hosts, be with us yet,
Lest we forget – lest we forget!

For heathen heart that puts her trust
  In reeking tube and iron shard,
All valiant dust that builds on dust,
  And guarding, calls not Thee to guard.
For frantic boast and foolish word –
  Thy mercy on Thy People, Lord!

Motoring Days

Kipling fell in love with the early motor cars, enabling him to explore Sussex more thoroughly than he could possibly have managed otherwise. It probably doesn't need saying that he was no reckless Mr Toad in his enthusiasm. For one thing he didn't drive the vehicles himself: his eyesight was poor and he was sufficiently short of stature to require blocks to be attached to the chair in his study so that he could sit comfortably at the desk. He employed a succession of chauffeur-mechanics, among them one Fleck, who features in a letter to his son John: 'We burst a tyre at Haywards Heath coming home – quite in the old Fleck style. It was a hot day and she went off with a bang like a seven-pounder – blew out the inner tube and spread it like a piece of tripe all over the wheel. All the same Fleck's driving is a wonder and a revelation. He never checks; he never hurries; he never skids on a curve and he never says a word to anyone on the road.'

Moreover, in a further contrast with the famous Toad, Kipling was fascinated by what lay beneath the bonnet. This is of a piece with his interest in machinery of any kind, a trait which some readers have found off-putting when introduced into his fiction as a kind of manly knowingness about the 'real' world of work. There is a connection here with his eulogy of Burne-Jones, who he saw as a craftsman rather than an artist.

Certainly Kipling had good reason to know about the inner working of his cars, since the early ones were always breaking down. The first, purchased in 1901, was an American Locomobile – aptly named both for its own waywardness and for the torment it inflicted upon the author. To one friend he wrote despairingly, 'Yes – I have a motor. I have a hell and a half of a motor . . . I wish I could tell you all I thought about motors.'

His switch to Lanchesters made little difference (a model bought in 1904 'smells like a fried fish shop and spits her condenser water, boiling, over our knees') which makes an encomium to the manufacturers in 1904 one of the minor mysteries of the Kipling correspondence. He tells them that his new '12 h.p. water-cooled' model has run for six months 'without flaw or failure,' adding that 'during this time she has covered over 4,000 miles in cramped and hilly country, often with a full load of luggage on the water deck. She has never been out of order when I wanted her, she has never delayed me five minutes on the road, and no day has been too long nor any hill too steep for her powers. Her repairs since June have been confined to one or two igniter springs.'

It is impossible to suspect Kipling of shabbily twisting the facts for financial reward, and yet no other explanation offers itself. A far more honest opinion is given in a letter to his fellow novelist Henry James, after the Kiplings drove to Lamb House in Rye for lunch and, ignominiously, had to return home by train because 'Amelia' (he always gave them names) had given up the ghost.

James expressed an interest in buying a car himself, to which Kipling replied, 'Touching motors – and Amelia specially – it's not so easy as it looks – a sick motor.' He details the repairs carried out by an expert brought down to Rye from Birmingham, and closes with a palpable shrug: 'So there you are and now you can keep a motor or not as you please.'

One of Kipling's Rolls-Royces can be seen (behind glass) in the garage at Bateman's.

Letter to James M. Conland, July 24, 1900

When we came back [from South Africa] I wrote a few stories about certain aspects of the war and then I lay off and was idle. The real reason was that we took to a motor – an old hired thing with a young hired man to drive it – and we have been exploring all Sussex County. It's just the kind of play that would delight you – a cross between steering a boat and driving an engine. But England being crowded with small and fascinating villages one never knows from one minute to the next what one will find. We go out together, the wife and I, after breakfast, get out twenty or thirty miles, lunch at some sort of hotel and come home in the cool of the evening. Our pretence is that we are hunting for a new house, but as a matter of fact we simply lounge around and get the skin peeled off our noses by the sun. I wish you were here for a spin with us. We have, of course, had one or two rather narrow shaves: for the cart horse of these parts is a trifle raw to the machine and it scares him.

From 'Something of Myself'

All this busy while the Committee of Ways and means kept before them the hope of a house of their very own – a real House in which to settle down for keeps – and took trains on rails and horsed carriages of the age to seek it. Our adventures were many and sometimes grim – as when a 'comfortable nursery' proved to be a dark padded cell at the end of a discreet passage! Thus we quested for two or three years, till one summer day a friend cried at our door: 'Mr Harmsworth has just brought round on those those motor-car things. Come and try it!'

It was a twenty-minute trip. We returned white with dust and dizzy with noise. But the poison worked from that hour. Somehow, an enterprising Brighton agency hired us a victoria-hooded, carriage-sprung, carriage-braked, single-cylinder, belt-driven, fixed-ignition Embryo which, at times, could cover eight miles an hour. Its hire, including 'driver' was three and a half guineas a week. The beloved Aunt, who feared nothing created, said 'Me too!' So we three house-hunted together taking risks of ignorance that made me shudder through after-years. But we went to Arundel and back, which was sixty miles, and returned in the same ten-hour day! We, and a few other desperate pioneers, took the first shock of outraged public opinion. Earls stood up in their belter barouches and cursed us. Gipsies, governess-carts, brewery waggons – all the world except the poor patient horses who would have been quite quiet if let alone joined in the commination service, and the *Times* leaders on 'motor-cars' were eolithic in outlook.

Then I bought me a steam-car called a Locomobile, whose nature and attributes I faithfully drew in a tale called 'Steam Tactics'. She reduced us to the limits of fatigue and hysteria, all up and down Sussex. Next came the earliest Lanchester, whose springing, even at that time, was perfect. But no designer, manufacturer, owner, nor chauffeur knew anything about anything. The heads of the Lanchester firm would, after furious telegrams, visit us as friends (we were all friends in those days) and sit round our hearth speculating Why What did That. Once, the proud designer – she was his newest baby – took me as far as Worthing, where she fainted opposite a vacant building-lot. This we paved completely with every other fitting that she possessed ere we got at her trouble. We then re-assembled her, a two hours' job. After which, she spat boiling water over our laps, but we stuffed a rug into the geyser and so spouted home.

Letter to John S. Phillips, July 4, 1901
As to the Locomobile herself, she is at present a Holy Terror. If ever you meet Amzi Lorenze Barber, who I gather is President of the Company, you may tell him that I yearn for his presence on the driving seat with me.

I suppose she will settle down some day to her conception of duty but just now her record is one of eternal and continuous breakdown. She disgraced us on June 26th when I took two friends over 13 miles of flat road. The pumps failed to lift and we had to pump dolefully every few miles home. Also she took to blowing through her pistons.

We overhauled her on June 27th (all the day). She did some run-about trips on June 28th. On June 29th we laid out a trip 19 miles out and back. I took the wife. She (the Loco) betrayed us foully 12 miles out – blew through her cylinders, leaked and laid down. It was a devil of a day. It ended in coming home by train. The wife nearly dead with exhaustion.

On June 30th I telephoned up to town and got the London agents to send down a man to overhaul. She needed repacking throughout, and the main steam valve leaked. (Another day off.) . . . Went up to town on the 1st. Came down on the second July. She covered the five miles from the station to my home in fine form.

Yesterday, July 3, I went for an evening trip – a few miles only along the road. Her steam was beautiful, but she shut down her fire automatically, and amid the jeers of Brighton we crawled to the Brighton repair shop, where we left her. The explanation was that her petrol pipe was choked. She apparently must be taken to pieces every time anything goes wrong with her. She is today in the shop being cleaned, and I shall be lucky if I get her tomorrow night.

I tell you these things that you may think once or twice ere you get a Locomobile. It is quite true that she is noiseless, but so is a corpse, and one does not get much fun out of a corpse.

Is McClure's open to a story of her performance – say 5000 words under caption 'Locoed'? If the worst comes to the worst I may reimburse myself that way for the cost of her repairs during the past ten days.

It isn't as if we wanted her for long tours – isn't as if we ever tried to get more than 10 miles an hour out of her. We got her for a carriage – a refined and lady-like carriage – and we treat her on that basis. Her lines are lovely; her form is elegant; the curves of her buggy-top are alone worth the price of admission, but – as a means of propulsion she is today a nickleplated fraud. I guess Amzi Lorenzo goes about the world in a B'way surface car.

Yours locomobiously but always sincerely . . .

THE COMPLETE MOTORIST

Kipling wrote an article in letter form for 'The Complete Motorist', published in 1904, at the request of its editor, Filson Young.

I like motoring because I have suffered for its sake. I began seven years ago in the days of tube ignition, when 6 h.p. was reckoned fair allowance for a touring car, and fifteen miles an hour was something to talk about. My agonies, shames, delays, rages, chills, parboilings, road-walkings, water-drawings, burns and starvations . . . all went to make your car today safe and comfortable . . .

'. . . the garden where Jack Cade was killed.' A memorial to the rebel leader stands by the road at Cade Street, near Heathfield.

Nowadays my car helps me to live at a decent distance from any town without sacrificing what house agents call the amenities. I am rid of the whole tribe of coachmen, saddlers, corn-dealers, smiths and vets. I can catch me a train anywhere within fifteen miles when I please, and not when the Jenny's hind leg or Jack's cough is better; and if I visit, I do so as a free agent, making my own arrangements for coming and going. In all cross-country journeys I am from one to four hours quicker than the local train service. On main line routes I hold my own – in greater comfort than the railway can give me – up to forty miles.

But the chief end of my car, so far as I am concerned, is the discovery of England. To me it is a land full of stupefying marvels and mysteries; and a day in the car in an English county is a day in some fairy museum where all the exhibits are alive and real and yet none the less delightfully mixed up with books. For instance, in six hours I can go from the land of the Ingoldsby Legends by way of the Norman Conquest and the Barons' War into Richard Jefferies' country, and so through the Regency, one of Arthur Young's less known tours, and Celia's Arbour, into Gilbert White's territory.

Horses, after all, are only horses; but the car is a time-machine on which one can slide from one century to another at no more trouble than the pushing forward of a lever. On a morning I have seen the Assizes, javelin-men and all, come into a cathedral town; by noon I was skirting a new-built convent for expelled French nuns; before sundown I was watching the Channel Fleet off Selsey Bill, and after dark I nearly broke a fox's back on a Roman road.

You who were born and bred in the land naturally take such trifles for granted, but to me it is still miraculous that if I want petrol in a hurry I must either pass the place where Sir John Lade lived, or the garden where Jack Cade was killed. In Africa one has only to put the miles under and go on; but in England the dead, twelve coffin deep, clutch hold of my wheels at every turn, till I sometimes wonder that the very road does not bleed.

That is the real joy of motoring – the exploration of this amazing England.

28

THEY

The narrator of this fine short story, from Kipling's 1904 collection 'Traffics and Discoveries', is a version of the author himself, travelling in an untrustworthy car from the far east of Sussex to a remote spot in the west. The countryside is vividly described, the changes in the landscape evoked by brilliant flashes of detail.

This is a ghost story which – 'the little brushing kiss fell in the centre of my palm' – is itself haunted by the death of his daughter Josephine in 1899. Kipling admitted that its ending was 'susceptible of several interpretations'. Although attracted by the supernatural, he distrusted mediums and perhaps feared for his mental balance should he be drawn into their ambience: his sister Trix suffered bouts of insanity and all his life he felt that he was himself dangerously close to the edge.

The hamlet with supposed American connections is Washington, which lies under the 'great Down' of Chanctonbury Ring.

One view called me to another; one hill-top to its fellow, half across the county, and since I could answer at no more trouble than the snapping forward of a lever, I let the county flow under my wheels. The orchid-studded flats of the East gave way to the thyme, ilex and grey grass of the Downs; these again to the rich cornland and fig-trees of the lower coast, where you carry the beat of the tide on your left hand for fifteen level miles; and when at last I turned inland through a huddle of rounded hills and woods I had run myself clean out of my known marks.

Beyond that precise hamlet which stands godmother to the capital of the United States, I found hidden villages where bees, the only things awake, boomed in eighty-foot lindens that overhung grey Norman churches; miraculous brooks diving under stone bridges built for heavier traffic than would ever vex them again; tithe-barns larger than their churches, and an old smithy that cried out aloud how it had once been a hall of the Knights of the Temple. Gipsies I found on a common where the gorse, bracken and heath fought it out together up a mile of Roman road; and a little farther on I disturbed a red fox rolling dog-fashion in the naked sunlight.

As the wooded hills closed about me I stood up in the car to take the bearings of that great Down whose ringed head is a landmark for fifty miles across the low countries. I judged that the lie of the country would

– Chanctonbury Ring –

bring me across some westward-running road that went to his feet, but I did not allow for the confusing veil of the woods. A quick turn plunged me first into a green cutting brim-full of liquid sunshine, next into a gloomy tunnel where last year's dead leaves whispered and scuffled about my tyres. The strong hazel stuff meeting overhead had not been cut for a couple of generations at least, nor had any axe helped the moss-cankered oak and beech to spring above them. Here the road changed frankly into a carpeted ride on whose brown velvet spent primrose-clumps showed like jade, and a few sickly, white-stalked bluebells nodded together. As the slope favoured I shut off the power and slid over the whirled leaves, expecting every moment to meet a keeper; but I only heard a jay, far off, arguing against the silence under the twilight of the trees.

Still the track descended. I was on the point of reversing and working my way back on the second speed ere I ended in some swamp, when I saw sunshine through the tangle ahead and lifted the brake.

It was down again at once. As the light beat across my face more fore-wheels took the turf of a great still lawn from which sprang horsemen ten feet high with levelled lances, monstrous peacocks, and sleek round-headed maids of honour – blue, black and glistening – all of clipped yew. Across the lawn – the marshalled woods besieged it on three sides – stood an ancient house of lichened and weather-worn stone, with mullioned windows and roofs of rose-red tile. It was flanked by semi-circular walls, also rose-red, that closed the lawn on the fourth side, and at their feet a box hedge grew man-high. There were doves on the roof about the slim brick chimneys, and I caught a glimpse of an octagonal dove-house behind the screening wall.

Here, then, I stayed; a horseman's green spear laid at my breast; held by the exceeding beauty of that jewel in that setting.

'If I am not packed off for a trespasser, or if this knight does not ride a wallop at me,' thought I, 'Shakespeare and Queen Elizabeth at least must come out of that half-open garden door and ask me to tea.'

A child appeared at an upper window, and I thought the little thing waved a friendly hand. But it was to call a companion, for presently another bright head showed. Then I heard a laugh among the yew-peacocks, and turning to make sure (till then I had been watching the house only) I saw the silver of a fountain behind a hedge thrown up against the sun. The doves on the roof cooed to the cooing water; but between the two notes I caught the utterly happy chuckle of a child absorbed in some light mischief.

The garden door – heavy oak sunk deep in the thickness of the wall – opened further; a woman in a big garden hat set foot slowly on the time-hollowed stone step and as slowly walked across the turf. I was forming some apology when she lifted up her head and I saw that she was blind.

'I heard you,' she said. 'Isn't that a motor car?'

'I'm afraid I've made a mistake in my road. I should have turned off up above – I never dreamed – ' I began.

'But I'm very glad. Fancy a motor car coming into the garden! It will be such a treat – ' She turned and made as though looking about her. 'You – you haven't seen any one, have you – perhaps?'

'No one to speak to, but the children seemed interested at a distance.'

'Which?'

'I saw a couple up at the window just now, and I think I heard a little chap in the grounds.'

'Oh, lucky you!' she cried, and her face brightened. 'I hear them, of course, but that's all. You've seen them and heard them?'

'Yes,' I answered. 'And if I know anything of children, one of them's having a beautiful time by the fountain yonder. Escape, I should imagine.'

'You're fond of children?'

I gave her one or two reasons why I did not altogether hate them.

'Of course, of course,' she said. 'Then you understand. Then you won't think it foolish if I ask you to take your car through the gardens, once or twice – quite slowly. I'm sure they'd like to see it. They see so little, poor things. One tries to make their life pleasant, but – ' she threw out her hands towards the woods. 'We're so out of the world here.'

'That will be splendid,' I said. 'But I can't cut up your grass.'

She faced to the right. 'Wait a minute,' she said. 'We're at the South gate, aren't we? Behind those peacocks there's a flagged path. We call it the Peacocks' Walk. You can't see it from here, they tell me, but if you squeeze along by the edge of the wood you can turn at the first peacock and get on to the flags.'

It was sacrilege to wake that dreaming house-front with the clatter of machinery, but I swung the car to clear the turf, brushed along the edge of the wood and turned in on the broad stone path where the fountain-basin lay like one star-sapphire.

'May I come too?' she cried. 'No, please don't help me. They'll like it better if they see me.'

She felt her way lightly to the front of the car, and with one foot on the step she called: 'Children, oh, children! Look and see what's going to happen!'

The voice would have drawn lost souls from the Pit, for the yearning that underlay its sweetness, and I was not surprised to hear an answering shout beyond the yews. It must have been the child by the fountain, but he fled at our approach, leaving a little toy boat in the water. I saw the glint of his blue blouse among the still horsemen.

Very disposedly we paraded the length of the walk and at her request backed again. This time the child had got the better of his panic, but stood far off and doubting.

'The little fellow's watching us,' I said. 'I wonder if he'd like a ride.'

'They're very shy still. Very shy. But, oh, lucky you to be able to see them! Let's listen.'

I stopped the machine at once, and the humid stillness, heavy with the scent of box, cloaked us deep. Shears I could hear where some gardener was clipping; a mumble of bees and broken voices that might have been the doves.

'Oh, unkind!' she said weariedly.

'Perhaps they're only shy of the motor. The little maid at the window looks tremendously interested.'

'Yes?' She raised her head. 'It was wrong of me to say that. They are really fond of me. It's the only thing that makes life worth living – when they're fond of you, isn't it? I daren't think what the place would be without them. By the way, is it beautiful?'

'I think it is the most beautiful place I have ever seen.'

'So they all tell me. I can feel it, of course, but that isn't quite the same thing.'

'Then have you never – ?' I began, but stopped abashed.

'Not since I can remember. It happened when I was only a few months old, they tell me. And yet I must remember something, else how could I dream about colours. I see light in my dreams, and colours, but I never see them. I only hear them just as I do when I'm awake.'

'It's difficult to see faces in dreams. Some people can, but most of us haven't the gift,' I went on, looking up at the window where the child stood all but hidden.

'I've heard that too,' she said. 'And they tell me that one never sees a dead person's face in a dream. Is that true?'

'I believe it is – now I come to think of it.'

'But how is it with yourself – yourself?' The blind eyes turned towards me.

'I have never seen the faces of my dead in any dream,' I answered.

'Then it must be as bad as being blind.'

The sun had dipped behind the woods and the long shades were possessing the insolent horsemen one by one. I saw the light die from off the top of a glossy-leafed lance and all the brave hard green turn to soft black. The house, accepting another day at end, as it had accepted an hundred thousand gone, seemed to settle deeper into its rest among the shadows.

'Have you ever wanted to?' she said after the silence.

'Very much sometimes,' I replied. The child had left the window as the shadows closed upon it.

'Ah! So've I, but I don't suppose it's allowed . . . Where d'you live?'

'Quite the other side of the county – sixty miles and more, and I must be going back. I've come without my big lamps.'

'But it's not dark yet. I can feel it.'

'I'm afraid it will be by the time I get home. Could you lend me someone to set me on my road at first? I've utterly lost myself.'

'I'll send Madden with you to the cross-roads. We are so out of the world, I don't wonder you were lost! I'll guide you round to the front of the house; but you will go slowly, won't you, till you're out of the grounds? It isn't foolish, do you think?'

'I promise you I'll go like this,' I said, and let the car start herself down the flagged path.

We skirted the left wing of the house, whose elaborately cast lead guttering alone was worth a day's journey; passed under a great rose-grown gate in the red wall, and so round to the high front of the house, which in beauty and stateliness as much excelled the back as that all others I had seen.

'Is it so very beautiful?' she said wisftfully when she heard my raptures. 'And you like the lead figures too? There's the old azalea garden behind. They say that this place must have been made for children. Will you help me out, please? I should like to come with you as far as the cross-roads, but I mustn't leave them. Is that you, Madden? I want you to show this gentleman the way to the cross-roads. He has lost his way, but – he has seen them.'

A butler appeared noiselessly at the miracle of old oak that must be called the front door, and slipped aside to put on his hat. She stood looking at me with open blue eyes in which no sight lay, and I saw for the first time that she was beautiful.

'Remember,' she said quietly, 'if you are fond of them you will come again,' and disappeared within the house.

The butler in the car said nothing till we were nearly at the lodge gates, where catching a glimpse of blue blouse in a shrubbery I swerved amply lest the devil that leads little boys to play should drag me into child murder.

'Excuse me,' he asked of a sudden, 'but why did you do that, Sir?'

'The child yonder.'

'Our young gentleman in blue?'

'Of course.'

'He runs about a good deal. Did you see him by the fountain, Sir?'

'Oh, yes, several times. Do we turn here?'

'Yes, Sir. And did you 'appen to see them upstairs too?'

'At the upper window? Yes.'

'Was that before the mistress come out to speak to you, Sir?'

'A little before that. Why d'you want to know?'

He paused a little. 'Ony to make sure that – that they had seen the car, Sir, because with children running about, though I'm sure you're driving particularly careful, there might be an accident. That was all, Sir. Here are the cross-roads. You can't miss your way from now on. Thank you, Sir, but that isn't our custom, not with – '

'I beg your pardon,' I said, and thrust away the British silver.

'Oh, it's quite right with the rest of 'em as a rule. Goodbye, Sir.'

He retired into the armour-plated conning-tower of his caste and walked away. Evidently a butler solicitous for the honour of his house, and interested, probably through a maid, in the nursery.

Once beyond the signposts at the cross-roads I looked back, but the crumpled hills interlaced so jealously that I could not see where the house had lain. When I asked its name at a cottage along the road, the fat woman who sold sweetmeats there gave me to understand that people with motor cars had small right to live – much less to 'go about talking like carriage folk'. They were not a pleasant-mannered community.

When I retraced my route on the map that evening I was little wiser. Hawkin's Old Farm appeared to be the Survey title of the place, and the old County Gazetteer, generally so ample, did not allude to it. The big house of those parts was Hodnington Hall, Georgian with early Victorian embellishments, as an atrocious steel engraving attested. I carried my difficulty to a neighbour – a deep-rooted tree of that soil – and he gave me a name of a family which conveyed no meaning.

A month or so later I went again, or it may have been that my car took the road of her own volition. She over-ran the fruitless Downs, threaded every turn of the maze of lanes below the hills, drew through the high-walled woods, impenetrable in their full leaf, came out at the cross-roads where the butler had left me, and a little farther on developed an internal trouble which forced me to turn her in on a grass way-waste that cut into a summer-silent hazel wood. So far as I could make sure by the sun and a six-inch Ordnance map, this should be the road flank of that wood which I had first explored from the heights above. I made a mighty serious business of my repairs and a glittering shop of my repair kit, spanners, pump and the like, which I spread out orderly upon a rug. It was a trap to catch all childhood, for on such a day, I argued, the children would not be far off. When I paused in my work I listened, but the wood was so full of the noises of summer (though the birds had mated) that I could not at first distinguish these from the tread of small cautious feet stealing across the dead leaves. I rang my bell in an alluring manner, but the feet fled, and I repented, for to a child a sudden noise is very real terror.

I must have been at work half an hour when I heard in the wood the voice of the blind woman crying: 'Children, oh, children! Where are you?' and the stillness made slow to close on the perfection of that cry. She came towards me, half feeling her way between the tree boles, and though a child, it seemed, clung to her skirt, it swerved into the leafage like a rabbit as she drew nearer.

'Is that you?' she said, 'from the other side of the county?'

'Yes, it's me from the other side of the county.'

'Then why didn't you come through the upper woods? They were there just now.'

'They were here a few minutes ago. I expect they knew my car had broken down, and came to see the fun.'

'Nothing serious, I hope? How do cars break down?'

'In fifty different ways. Only mine has chosen the fifty-first.'

She laughed merrily at the tiny joke, cooed with delicious laughter, and pushed her hat back.

'Let me hear,' she said.

'Wait a moment,' I cried, 'and I'll get you a cushion.'

She set her foot on the rug all covered with spare parts, and stopped above it eagerly. 'What delightful things!' The hands through which she saw glanced in the chequered sunlight. 'A box here – another box! Why, you've arranged them like playing shop!'

'I confess now that I put it out to attract them. I don't need half those things really.'

'How nice of you! I heard your bell in the upper wood. You say they were here before that?'

'I'm sure of it. Why are they so shy? That little fellow in blue who was with you just now ought to have got over his fright. He's been watching me like a Red Indian.'

'It must have been your bell,' she said. 'I heard one of them go past me in trouble when I was coming down. They're shy – so shy even with me.' She turned her face over her shoulder and cried again: 'Children, oh, children! Look and see!'

'They must have gone off together on their own affairs,' I suggested, for there was a murmur behind us of lowered voices broken by the sudden squeaking giggles of childhood. I returned to my tinkerings and she leaned forward, her chin on her hand, listening interestedly.

'How many are they?' I said at last. The work was finished, but I saw no reason to go.

Her forehead puckered a little in thought. 'I don't quite know,' she said simply. 'Sometimes more – sometimes less. They come and stay with me because I love them, you see.'

'That must be very jolly,' I said, replacing a drawer, and as I spoke I heard the inanity of my answer.

'You – you aren't laughing at me?' she cried. 'I – I haven't any of my own. I never married. People laugh at me sometimes about them because – because – '

'Because they're savages,' I returned. 'It's nothing to fret for. That sort laugh at everything that isn't in their own fat lives.'

'I don't know. How should I? I only don't like being laughed at about them. It hurts; and when one can't see . . . I don't want to seem silly,' her chin quivered like a child's as she spoke, 'but we blindies have only one skin, I think. Everything outside hits straight at our souls. It's different with you. You've such good defences in your eyes – looking out – before anyone can really pain you in your soul. People forget that with us.'

I was silent, reviewing that inexhaustible matter – the more than inherited (since it is also carefully taught) brutality of the Christian people, besides which the mere heathendom of the West Coast nigger is clean and restrained. It led me a long distance into myself.

'Don't do that!' she said of a sudden, putting her hands before her eyes.

'What?'

She made a gesture with her hand.

'That! It's – it's purple and black. Don't! That colour hurts!'

'But how in the world do you know about colours?' I exclaimed, for here was a revelation indeed.

'Colours as colours?' she asked.

'No. Those Colours which you saw just now.'

'You know as well as I do,' she laughed, 'else you wouldn't have asked that question. They aren't in the world at all. They're in you – when you went so angry.'

'D'you mean a dull purplish patch, like port wine mixed with ink?' I said.

'I've never seen ink or port wine, but the colours aren't mixed. They can separate – all separate.'

'Do you mean black streaks and jags across the purple?'

She nodded. 'Yes – if they are like this,' and zig-zagged her finger again, 'but it's more red than purple – that bad colour.'

'And what are the colours at the top of the – whatever you see?'

Slowly she leaned forward and traced on the rug the figure of the Egg itself.

'I see them so,' she said, pointing with a grass stem, 'white, green, yellow, red, purple, and when people are angry or bad, black across the red – as you were just now.'

'Who told you anything about it – in the beginning?' I demanded.

'About the colours? No one. I used to ask what colours were when I was little – in tablecovers and curtains and carpets you see – because some colours hurt me and some made me happy. People told me; and when I got older that was how I saw people.' Again she traced the outline of the Egg which it is given to very few of us to see.

'All by yourself?' I repeated.

'All by myself. There wasn't anyone else. I only found out afterwards that other people did not see the Colours.'

She leaned against the tree-bole plaiting and unplaiting chance-plucked grass stems. The children in the wood had drawn nearer. I could see them with the tail of my eye frolicking like squirrels.

'Now I am sure you will never laugh at me,' she went on after a long silence. 'Nor at *them.*'

'Goodness! No!' I cried, jolted out of my train of thought. 'A man who laughs at a child – unless the child is laughing too – is a heathen!'

'I didn't mean that, of course. You'd never laugh at children, but I thought – I used to think – that perhaps you might laugh about them. So now I beg your pardon . . . What are you going to laugh at?'

I had made no sound, but she knew.

'At the notion of your begging my pardon. If you had done your duty as a pillar of the State and a landed proprietress you ought to have summoned me for trespass when I barged through your woods the other day. It was disgraceful of me – inexcusable.'

She looked at me, her head against the tree-trunk – long and steadfastly – this woman who could see the naked soul.

'How curious,' she half whispered. 'How very curious.'

'Why, what have I done?'

'You don't understand . . . and yet you understood about the Colours. Don't you understand?'

She spoke with a passion that nothing had justified, and I faced her bewilderedly as she rose. The children had gathered themselves in a roundel behind a bramble bush. One sleek head bent over something smaller, and the set of the little shoulderes told me that fingers were on lips. They, too, had some child's tremendous secret. I alone was hopelessly astray there in the broad sunlight.

'No,' I said, and shook my head as though the dead eyes could note.

'Whatever it is, I don't understand yet. Perhaps I shall later – if you'll let me come again.'

'You will come again,' she answered. 'You will surely come again and walk in the wood.'

'Perhaps the children will know me well enough by that time to let me play with them – as a favour. You know what children are like.'

'It isn't a matter of favour but of right,' she replied, and while I wondered what she meant, a dishevelled woman plunged round the bend of the road, loose-haired, purple, almost lowing with agony as she ran. It was my rude, fat friend of the sweetmeat shop. The blind woman heard and stepped forward. 'What is it, Mrs Madehurst?' she asked.

The woman flung her apron over her head and literally grovelled in the dust, crying that her grandchild was sick to death, that the local doctor was away fishing, that Jenny the mother was at her wits' end, and so forth, with repetitions and bellowings.

'Where's the nearest doctor?' I asked between paroxysms.

'Madden will tell you. Go round to the house and take him with you. I'll attend to this. Be quick!' She half supported the fat woman into the shade. In two minutes I was blowing all the horns of Jericho under the front of the House Beautiful, and Madden, in the pantry, rose to the crisis like a butler and a man.

A quarter of an hour at illegal speeds caught us a doctor five miles away. Within the half-hour we had decanted him, much interested in motors, at the door of the sweetmeat shop, and drew up the road to await the verdict.

'Useful things, cars,' said Madden, all man and no butler. 'If I'd have one when mine took sick she wouldn't have died.'

'How was it?' I asked.

'Croup. Mrs Madden was away. No one knew what to do. I drove eight miles in a tax-cart for the doctor. She was choked when we came back. This car'd ha' saved her. She'd have been close on ten now.'

'I'm sorry,' I said. 'I thought you were rather fond of children from what you told me going to the cross-roads the other day.'

'Have you seen 'em again, Sir – this mornin'?'

'Yes, but they're well broke to cars. I couldn't get any of them within twenty yards of it.'

He looked at me carefully as a scout considers a stranger – not as a menial should lift his eyes to his divinely appointed superior.

'I wonder why,' he said just above the breath that he drew.

We waited on. A light wind from the sea wandered up and down the long line of the woods, and the wayside grasses, whitened already with summer dust, rose and bowed in sallow waves.

A woman, wiping the suds off her arms, came out of the cottage next the sweetmeat shop.

'I've be'n listening' in de back-yard,' she said cheerily. 'He says Arthur's unaccountable bad. Did ye heare him shruck just now? Unaccountable bad. I reckon t'will come Jenny's turn to walk in de wood nex' week along, Mr Madden.'

'Excuse me, Sir, but your lap-robe is slipping,' said Madden deferentially. The woman started, dropped a curtsey, and hurried away.

'What does she mean by "walking in the wood"?' I asked.

'It must be some saying they use hereabouts. I'm from Norfolk myself,' said Madden. 'They're an independent lot in this county. She took you for a chauffeur, Sir.'

I saw the Doctor come out of the cottage followed by a draggle-tailed wench who clung to his arm as though he could make treaty for her with Death. 'Dat sort,' she wailed – 'dey're jut as much to us dat has 'em as if dey was lawful born. Just as much – just as much! An' God he'd be just as pleased if you saven 'un, Doctor. Don't take it from me. Miss Florence will tell ye de very same. Don't leave 'im, Doctor.'

'I know, I know,' said the man; 'but he'll be quiet for a while now. We'll get the nurse and the medicine as fast as we can.' He signalled me to come forward with the car, and I strove not to be privy to what followed; but I saw the girl's face, blotched and frozen with grief, and I felt the hand without a ring clutching at my knees when we moved away.

The Doctor was a man of some humour, for I remember he claimed my car under the Oath of Aesculapius, and used it and me without mercy. First we conveyed Mrs Madehurst and the blind woman to wait by the sick-bed till the nurse should come. Next we invaded a neat county town for prescriptions (the Doctor said the trouble was cerebro-spinal meningitis), and when the County Institute, banked and flanked with scared market cattle, reported itself out of nurses for the moment we literally flung ourselves loose upon the county. We conferred with the owners of great houses – magnates at the ends of overarching avenues whose big-boned womenfolk strode away from their tea-tables to listen to the imperious Doctor. At last a white-haired lady sitting under a cedar of Lebanon and surrounded by a court of magnificent Borzois – all hostile to motors – gave the Doctor, who received them as from a princess, written orders which we bore many miles at top speed, through a park, to a French nunnery, where we took over in exchange a pallid-faced and trembling Sister. She knelt at the bottom of the tonneau telling her beads without pause till, by short cuts of the Doctor's invention, we had her to the sweetmeat shop once more. It was a long afternoon crowded with mad episodes that rose and dissolved like the dust of our wheels; cross-sections of remote and incomprehensible lives through which we raced at right angles; and I went home in the dusk, wearied out, to dream of the clashing horns of cattle; round-eyed nuns walking in a garden of graves; pleasant tea-parties beneath shady trees; the carbolic-scented, grey-painted corridors of the County Institute; the steps of shy children in the wood, and the hands that clung to my knees as the motor began to move.

I had intended to return in a day or two, but it pleased Fate to hold me from that side of the county, on many pretexts, till the elder and the wild rose had fruited. There came at last a brilliant day, swept clear from the south-west, that brought the hills within hand's reach – a day of unstable airs and high filmy clouds. Through no merit of my own I was free, and set the car for the third time on that known road. As I reached the crest of the Downs I felt the soft air change, saw it glaze under the sun; and, looking down at the sea, in that instant beheld the blue of the channel turn through polished silver and dulled steel to dingy pewter. A laden collier hugging the coast steered outward for deeper water, and, across copper-coloured haze, I saw sails rise one by one on the anchored fishing-fleet. In a deep dene behind me an eddy of sudden wind drummed through sheltered oaks, and spun aloft the first dry sample of autumn leaves. When I reached the beach road the sea-fog fumed over the brick-fields, and the tide was telling all the groynes of the gale beyond Ushant. In less than an hour summer England vanished in chill grey. We were again the shut island of the North, all the ships of the world bellowing at our perilous gates; and between their outcries ran the piping of bewildered gulls. My cap dripped moisture, the folds of the rug held it in pools or sluiced it away in runnels, and the salt-rime stuck to my lips.

Inland the smell of autumn loaded the thickened fog among the trees, and the drip became a continuous shower. Yet the late flowers – mallow of the wayside, scabious of the field, and dahlia of the garden – showed gay in the mist, and beyond the sea's breath there was little sign of decay in the leaf. Yet in the villages the house doors were all open, and bare-legged, bare-headed children sat at ease on the damp doorsteps to shout 'pip-pip' at the stranger.

I made bold to call at the sweetmeat shop, where Mrs Madehurst met me with a fat woman's hospitable tears. Jenny's child, she said, had died two days after the nun had come. It was, she felt, best out of the way, even though insurance offices, for reasons which she did not pretend to follow, would not willingly insure such stray lives. 'Not but what Jenny didn't tend to Arthur as though he'd come all proper at de end of de first year – like Jenny herself.' Thanks to Miss Florence, the child had been buried with a pomp which, in Mrs Madehurst's opinion, more than covered the small irregularity of its birth. She described the coffin, within and without, the glass hearse and the evergreen lining of the grave.

'But how's the mother?' I asked.

'Jenny? Oh, she'll get over it. I've felt dat way with one or two o' my own. She'll get over. She's walkin' in de wood now.'

'In this weather?'

Mrs Madehurst looked at me with narrowed eyes across the counter.

'I dunno but it opens de 'eart like. Yes, it opens de 'eart. Dat's where losin' and bearin' comes so alike in de long run we do say.'

Now the wisdom of the old wives is greater than that of all the Fathers, and this last oracle sent me thinking so extendedly as I went up the road, that I nearly ran over a woman and a child at the wooded corner by the lodge gates of the House Beautiful.

'Awful weather!' I cried, as I slowed dead for the turn.

'Not so bad,' she answered placidly out of the fog. 'Mine's used to 'un. You'll find yours indoors, I reckon.'

Indoors, Madden received me with professional courtesy, and kind inquiries for the health of the motor, which he would put under cover.

I waited in a still, nut-brown hall, pleasant with late flowers and wrmed with a delicious wood fire – a place of good influence and great peace. (Men and women may sometimes, after great effort, achieve a creditable lie; but the house, which is their temple, cannot say anything save the truth of those who have lived in it.) A child's cart and a doll lay on the black-and-white floor, where a rug had been kicked back. I felt that the children had only just hurried away – to hide themselves, most like – in the many turns of the great adzed staircase that climbed steadily out of the hall, or to crouch and gaze behind the lions and roses of the carven gallery above. Then I heard her voice above me, singing as the blind sing – from the soul:

> In the pleasant orchard-closes

And all my early summer came back at the call.

> In the pleasant orchard-closes,
>   God bless all our gains say we –
> But may God bless all our losses,
>   Better suits with our degree.

She dropped the marring fifth line, and repeated –

> Better suits with our degree!

I saw her lean over the gallery, her linked hands white as pearl against the oak.

'Is that you – from the other side of the county?' she called.

'Yes, me – from the other side of the county,' I answered, laughing.

'What a long time before you had to come here again.' She ran down the stairs, one hand lightly touching the broad rail. 'It's two months and four days. Summer's gone!'

'I meant to come before, but Fate prevented.'

'I knew it. Please do something to that fire. They won't let me play with it, but I can feel it's behaving badly. Hit it!'

I looked on either side of the deep fireplaces, and found but a half-charred hedge-stake with which I punched a black log into flame.

'It never goes out, day or night,' she said, as though explaining. 'In case anyone comes in with cold toes, you see.'

'It's even lovelier inside than it was out,' I murmured. The red light poured itself along the age-polished dusky panels till the Tudor roses and lions of the gallery took colour and motion. An old eagle-topped convex mirror gathered the picture into its mysterious heart, distorting afresh the distorted shadows, and curving the gallery lines into the curves of a ship. The day was shutting down in half a gale as the fog turned to stringy scud. Through the uncurtained mullions of the broad window I could see the valiant horsemen of the lawn rear and recover against the wind that taunted them with legions of dead leaves.

'Yes, it must be beautiful,' she said. 'Would you like to go over it? There's still enough light upstairs.'

I followed her up the unflinching, waggon-wide staircase to the gallery whence opened the thin fluted Elizabethan doors.

'Feel how they put the latch low down for the sake of the children.' She sung a light door inward.

'By the way, where are they?' I asked. 'I haven't even heard them today.'

She did not answer at once. Then, 'I can only hear them,' she replied softly. 'This is one of their rooms – everything ready, you see.'

She pointed into a heavily-timbered room. There were little low gate tables and children's chairs. A doll's house, its hooked front half open, faced a great dappled rocking-horse, from whose padded saddle it was but a child's scramble to the broad window-seat overlooking the lawn. A toy gun lay in a corner beside a gilt wooden cannon.

'Surely they've only just gone,' I whispered. In the failing light a door creaked cautiously. I heard the rustle of a frock and the patter of feet – quick feet through a room beyond.

'I heard that,' she cried triumphantly. 'Did you? Children, oh, children! Where are you?'

The voice filled the walls that held it lovingly to the last perfect note, but there came no answering shout such as I had heard in the garden. We hurried on from room to oak-floored room; up a step here, down three steps there; among a maze of passages; always mocked by our quarry. One might as well have tried to work an unstopped warren with a single ferret. There were bolt-holes innumerable – recesses in walls, embrasures of deep-slitten windows now darkened, whence they could start up behind us; and abandoned fireplaces, six feet deep in the masonry, as well as the tangle of communicating doors. Above all, they had the twilight for their helper in our game. I had caught one or two joyous chuckles of evasion, and once or twice had seen the silhouette of a child's frock against some darkening window at the end of a passage; but we returned empty-handed to the gallery, just as a middle-aged woman was setting a lamp in its niche.

'No, I haven't seen her either this evening, Miss Florence,' I heard her say, 'but that Turpin he says he wants to see you about his shed.'

'Oh, Mr Turpin must want to see me very badly. Tell him to come to the hall, Mrs Madden.'

I looked down into the hall whose only light was the dulled fire, and deep in the shadow I saw them at last. They must have slipped down while we were in the passages, and now thought themselves perfectly hidden behind an old gilt leather screen. By child's law, my fruitless chase was as good as an introduction, but since I had taken so much trouble I resolved to force them to come forward later by the simple trick, which children detest, of pretending not to notice them. They lay close, in a little huddle, no more than shadows except when a quick flame betrayed an outline.

'And now we'll have some tea,' she said. 'I believe I ought to have offered it you at first, but one doesn't arrive at manners somehow when one lives alone and is considered – h'm – peculiar.' Then with very pretty scorn, 'Would you like a lamp to see to eat by?'

'The firelight's much pleasanter, I think.' We descended into that delicious gloom and Madden brought tea.

I took my chair in the direction of the screen ready to surprise or be surprised as the game should go, and at her permission, since a hearth is always sacred, bent forward to play with the fire.

'Where do you get these beautiful short faggots from?' I asked idly. 'Why, they are tallies!'

'Of course,' she said. 'As I can't read or write I'm driven back on the early English tally for my accounts. Give me one and I'll tell you what it meant.'

I passed her an unburned hazel-tally, about a foot long, and she ran her thumb down the nicks.

'This is the milk-record for the home farm for the month of April last year, in gallons,' said she. 'I don't know what I should have done without tallies. An old forester of mine taught me the system. It's out of date now for every one else; but my tenants respect it. One of them's coming now to see me. Oh, it doesn't matter. He has no business here out of office hours. He's a greedy, ignorant man – very greedy, or – he wouldn't come here after dark.'

'Have you much land then?'

'Only a couple of hundred acres in hand, thank goodness. The other six hundred are nearly all let to folk who knew my folk before me, but this Turpin's quite a new man – and a highway robber.'

'But are you sure I shan't be – ?'

'Certainly not. You have the right. He hasn't any children.'

'Ah, the children!' I said, and slid my low chair back till it nearly touched the screen that hid them. 'I wonder whether they'll come out for me.'

There was a murmur of voices – Madden's and a deeper note – at the low, dark side door, and a ginger-headed canvas-gaitered giant of the unmistakable tenant-farmer type stumbled or was pushed in.

'Come to the fire, Mr Turpin,' she said.

'If – if you please, Miss, I'll be quite as well by the door.' He clung to the latch as he spoke like a frightened child. Of a sudden I realised that he was in the grip of some almost overpowering fear.

'Well?'

'About that new shed for the young stock – that was all. These first autumn storms settin' in . . . but I'll come again, Miss.' His teeth did not chatter much more than the door-latch.

'I think not,' she answered levelly. 'The new shed – m'm. What did my agent write you on the 15th?'

'I – fancied p'raps that if I came to see you – ma – man to man like, Miss. But – '

His eyes rolled into every corner of the room wide with horror. He half opened the door through which he had entered, but I noticed it shut again – from without and firmly.

'He wrote what I told him,' she went on. 'You are over-stocked already. Dunnett's Farm never carried more than fifty bullocks – even in Mr Wright's time. And he used cake. You've sixty-seven and you don't cake. You've broken the lease in that respect. You're dragging the heart out of the farm.'

'I'm – I'm getting some minerals – superphosphates – next week. I've as good as ordered a truck-load already. I'll go down to the station tomorrow about 'em. Then I can come and see you man to man like,

Miss, in the daylight . . . That gentleman's not going away, is he?' he almost shrieked.

I had only slid the chair a little farther back, reaching behind me to tap on the leather of the screen, but he jumped like a rat.

'No. Please attend to me, Mr Turpin.' She turned in her chair and faced him with his back to the door. It was an old and sordid little piece of scheming that she forced from him – his plea for the new cow-shed at his landlady's expense, that he might with the covered manure pay his next year's rent out of the valuation after, as she made clear, he had bled the enriched pastures to the bone. I could not but admire the intensity of his greed, when I saw him outfacing for its sake whatever terror it was that ran wet on his forehead.

I ceased to tap the leather – was, indeed, calculating the cost of the shed – when I felt my relaxed hand taken and turned softly between the soft hands of a child. So at last I had triumphed. In a moment I would turn and acquaint myself with those quick-footed wanderers . . .

The little brushing kiss fell in the centre of my palm – as a gift on which the fingers were, once, expected to close: as the all-faithful half-reproachful signal of a waiting child not used to neglect even when grown-ups were busiest – a fragment of the mute code devised very long ago.

Then I knew. And it was as though I had known from the first day when I looked across the lawn at the high window.

I heard the door shut. The woman turned to me in silence, and I felt that she knew.

What time passed after this I cannot say. I was roused by the fall of a log, and mechanically rose to put it back. Then I returned to my place in the chair very close to the screen.

'Now you understand,' she whispered, across the packed shadows.

'Yes, I understand – now. Thank you.'

'I – I only hear them.' She bowed her head in her hands. 'I have no right, you know – no other right. I have neither borne nor lost – neither borne nor lost!'

'Be very glad then,' said I, for my soul was torn open within me.
'Forgive me!'

She was still, and I went back to my sorrow and my joy.

'It was because I loved them so,' she said at last, brokenly. 'That was why it was, even from the first – even before I knew that they – they were all I should ever have. And I loved them so!'

She stretched out her arms to the shadows and the shadows within the shadow.

'They came because I loved them – because I needed them. I – I must have made them come. Was that wrong, think you?'

'No – no.'

'I – I grant you that the toys and – and all that sort of thing were nonsense, but – but I used to so hate empty rooms myself when I was little.' She pointed to the gallery. 'And the passages all empty . . . And how could I ever bear the garden door shut? Suppose – '

'Don't! For pity's sake, don't!' I cried. The twilight had brought a cold rain with gusty squalls that plucked at the leaded windows.

'And the same thing with keeping the fire in all night. I don't think it so foolish – do you?'

I looked at the broad brick hearth, saw, through tears, I believe, that there was no unpassable iron on or near it, and bowed my head.

'I did all that and lots of other things – just to make believe. Then they came. I heard them, but I didn't know that they were not mine by right till Mrs Madden told me – '

'The butler's wife? What?'

'One of them – I heard – she saw. And knew Hers! Not for me. I didn't know at first. Perhaps I was jealous. Afterwards, I began to understand that it was only because I loved them, not because – . . . Oh, you must bear or lose,' she said piteously. 'There is no other way – and yet they love me. They must! Don't they?'

There was no other sound in the room except the lapping voices of the fire, but we two listened intently, and she at least took comfort from what she heard. She recovered herself and half rose. I sat still in my chair by the screen.

'Don't think me a wretch to whine about myself like this, but – but I'm all in the dark, you know, and you can see.'

In truth I could see, and my vision confirmed me in my resolve, though that was like the very parting of spirit and flesh. Yet a little longer I would stay since it was the last time.

'You think it is wrong, then?' she cried sharply, though I had said nothing.

'Not for you. A thousand times no. For you it is right . . . I am grateful to you beyond words. For me it would be wrong. For me only . . . '

'Why?' she said, but passed her hand before her face as she had done at our second meeting in the wood. 'Oh, I see,' she went on simply as a child. 'For you it would be wrong.' Then with a little indrawn laugh. 'And, d'you remember, I called you lucky – once – at first. You who must never come here again!'

She left me to sit a little longer by the screen, and I heard the sound of her feet die out along the gallery above.

For the 'Daily Mail' Kipling wrote a (later expanded)
series of literary pastiches, 'The Muse Among the
Motors', including 'The Idiot Boy', after Wordsworth.

He wandered down the mountain grade
  Beyond the speed assigned –
A youth whom Justice often stayed
  And generally fined.

He went alone, that none might know
  If he could drive or steer.
Now he is in the ditch, and Oh!
  The differential gear!

LIFE AT BATEMAN'S

The Kiplings bought Bateman's at Burwash, in the far east of Sussex, in 1902, and Kipling was to spend the last 34 of his 70 years here. They had been looking for an isolated retreat, a sanctuary after the family troubles in Vermont, the death of little Josephine and the increasing nuisance of sightseers around the green at Rottingdean. What they found was a 17th century sandstone house deep in the wooded and 'secretive' Weald, probably built by an ironmaster (certainly so, as far as Kipling was concerned), with a mill and 33 acres (which would gradually be extended to more than 300 with the purchase of small neighbouring farms), but with no bathroom and no electricity.

Although they made improvements (introducing a turbine at the mill to light ten 60-watt bulbs for four hours each evening and, with the money from Kipling's Nobel prize in 1907, creating a pond and a rose garden in the grounds) they never installed a telephone. Indeed, the house was to be a byword for austerity with visitors.

These early years at Bateman's were fruitful for Kipling. He continued to travel – to South Africa and, from 1908, to Switzerland

Bateman's from the front.

for winter sports holidays. There were motor tours in France and visits to Venice and Egypt, too. His short story collections *Traffics and Discoveries* and *Actions and Reactions* were published in 1904 and 1909 respectively, and during this period he also wrote the two Sussex-based history volumes *Puck of Pook's Hill* and *Rewards and Fairies* (*pages 95–136*). *A Diversity of Creatures* would follow in 1917.

But the clouds were gathering. His mother died in 1909 and his father a year later – leaving him with responsibility for his afflicted sister Trix. And then came the war and the second family tragedy. Kipling had pulled strings to have their son John join the Irish Guards despite his poor eyesight. He disappeared at the Battle of Loos, and Kipling made strenuous efforts to discover what had happened to him long after it was clear that he must be dead.

The two-line epitaph 'Common Form' of 1919 has been cited as evidence of his guilt for 'sending' his son to the front, although John himself had certainly been determined to go:

> *If any question why we died,*
> *Tell them, because our fathers lied.*

Whatever torments he may have suffered over his part in John's enlistment, however, Kipling is here surely expressing a bitterness about a generation which had refused to act before war was inevitable – despite his ample warnings. Replying to a letter of condolence from his old friend Lionel 'Stalky' Dunsterville, he displays a chilling example of British stiff upper-lip: 'I'm sorry that all the years' work ended in that one afternoon but – lots of people are in our position – and it's something to have bred a man.'

Still the imperial warrior, he visited the Navy in England and Scotland, and the Army in France and Italy, throughout the war. When it was over he became one of the war grave commissioners, suggesting most of the moving commemorative words we see on the gravestones today, and throwing his weight behind the creation of the Tomb of the Unknown Soldier in Westminster Abbey.

Another epitaph, 'A Son', gives us the grief:

> *My son was killed while laughing at some jest. I would I knew*
> *What it was, and it might serve me in a time when jests are few.*

THE ONLY SHE

From 'Something of Myself'

> *Kipling's autobiography is notoriously unreliable, and his memory seems to be at fault here. Carrie's diary reveals that the first visit to Bateman's was by train and fly, because the car had broken down yet again.*

It was the heart-breaking Locomobile that brought us to the house called Bateman's. We had seen an advertisement of her, and we reached her down an enlarged rabbit-hole of a lane. At very first sight the Committee of Ways and Means said: 'That's her! The Only She! Make an honest woman of her – quick!' We entered and felt her Spirit – her Feng Shui – to be good. We went through every room and found no shadow of ancient regrets, stifled miseries, nor any menace, though the 'new' end of her was three hundred years old. To our woe the Owner said: 'I've just let it for twelve months.' We withdrew, each repeatedly telling the other than no sensible person would be found dead in the stuffy little valley where she stood. We lied thus while we pretended to look at other houses till, a year later, we saw her advertised again, and got her.

When all was signed and sealed, the seller said: 'Now I can ask you something. How are you going to manage about getting to and from the station? It's nearly four miles, and I've used two pair of horses on the hill here.' 'I'm thinking of using this sort of contraption,' I replied from my seat in – Jane Cakebread Lanchester, I think was her dishonourable name. 'Oh! Those things haven't come to stay!' he returned. Years afterwards I met him, and he confided that had he known what I had guessed, he would have asked twice the money. In three years from our purchase the railway station had passed out of our lives. In seven, I heard my chauffeur say to an under-powered visiting sardine-tin: 'Hills? There ain't any hills on the London road.'

Letter to John St Loe Strachey, September 7, 1902

> *After his success with the Rottingdean Rifle Club (one of its triumphs is recorded here), Kipling wanted Bateman's to play its part in training the soldiers of the future.*

Yes, it's all our own; including a mill which was paying taxes in 1296! At present the tenant is growing hops, but as soon as he gets out I want to suppress that gambling (for hop-growing is more speculative than horseracing) and lay all down in grass.

When you come down, as you will, we'll go over the whole place (it's only about 30 acres) and see what we can do towards a spot for a camp . . . Now what the men want is camps if only for a fortnight – camps where they can dig latrines and trenches and pitch tents. The Rottingdean R.C. has just bust the Essex Volunteers and a team of amateurs from, I think, the Artists.

To Charles Eliot Norton, November 30–December 8, 1902
I don't know whether you know of our last transmigration. We left Rottingdean because Rottingdean was getting too populated; though we didn't want to part from Aunt Georgie. Then we discovered England which we had never done before (Rottingdean isn't England: it's the downs) and went to live in it.

England is a wonderful land. It is the most marvellous of all foreign countries that I have ever been in. It is made up of trees and green fields and mud and the Gentry: and at last I'm one of the Gentry! – I'll take a new pen and explain.

Behold us the lawful owners of a grey stone lichened house – A.D. 1634 over the door – beamed, panelled, with old oak staircase all untouched and unfaked. Heaven looked after it in the dissolute times of mid-Victorian restoration and caused the Vicar to send his bailiff to live in it for 40 years; and he lived in peaceable filth and left everything as he found it.

It is a good and peaceable place standing in terraced lawns nigh to a walled garden of old red brick and two fat-headed old oasthouses with red brick stomachs and an aged silver grey oak dovecot on top. There is what they call a river at the bottom of the lawn. It appears in all the maps and that, except after very heavy rain, is the only place where it puts in any appearance. Normally you hunt for it with a pole through alder bushes, but in flood time (so we are told) it runs about all over the little valley. It's name is the Dudwell, and it is quite ten feet wide.

The oasthouses at Bateman's.

But I think you'd like the inside of the house if you were here. There is a black and white tiled hall all panelled to the naked beamed ceiling and the doors out of it have stone heads and old oak frames – dark as teak. There is a deep window seat and a high leaded window with lots of the old greeny-glass panes left and a flap-table of Queen Elizabeth's time (the worst of the place is that it simply will not endure modern furniture) and benches and a stone arched fireplace backed by old Sussex ironwork. We burn wood in all the fires and the hall takes five-foot logs.

But in reality the house is little – not a manor house or a 'place' – just the kind of house that a successful Sussex iron master builded himself two hundred and fifty years ago. It hasn't a lodge or any nonsense of that kind. You walk up to the porch over a stone-paved path laid down in the turf and the cartroad runs within fifty yards of the front door. The rest is all fields and farms and to the southward one glorious sweep of woods. We coveted the place for two and half or three years and have loved it ever since our first sight of it.

HARNESSING THE MILL

From 'Something of Myself'

The House was not of a type to present to servants by lamp or candle-light. Hence electricity, which in 1902 was a serious affair. We chanced, at a week-end visit, to meet Sir William Willcocks, who had designed the Assouan Dam – a trifling affair on the Nile. Not to be over-crowed, we told him of our project for declutching the water-wheel from an ancient mill at the end of our garden, and using its microscopical mill-pond to run a turbine. That was enough!

'Dam?' said he. 'You don't know anything about dams or turbines. I'll come and look.' That Monday morn he came with us, explored the brook and the mill-sluit, and foretold truly the exact amount of horse-power that we should get out of our turbine – 'Four and a half and no more.' But he called me Egyptian names for the state of my brook, which, till then, I had deemed picturesque. 'It's all messed up with trees and bushes. Cut 'em down and slope the banks to one in three.' 'Lend me a couple of Fellahin Battalions and I'll begin,' I said.

He said also: 'Don't run your light cable on poles. Bury it.' So we got a deep-sea cable which had failed under test at twelve hundred volts – our voltage being one hundred and ten – and laid him in a trench from the Mill to the house, a full furlong, where he worked for a quarter of a century. At the end of that time he was a little fatigued, and the turbine had worn as much as one sixteenth of an inch on her bearings. So we

A turbine used water from the mill pond to provide Bateman's with electric light.

gave them both honourable demission – and never again got anything so faithful.

Of the little one-street village up the hill we only knew that, according to the guide-books, they came of a smuggling, sheep-stealing stock, brought more or less into civilisation within the past three generations. Those of them who worked for us, and who I presume would today be called 'labour', struck for higher pay than they had agreed on as soon as we were committed to our first serious works.

My foreman and general contractor, himself of their race, and soon to become our good friend, said: 'They think they've got ye. They think there's no harm in tryin' it.' There was not. I had sense enough to feel that most of them were artists and craftsmen, either in stone or timber, or wood-cutting, or drain-laying or – which is a gift – the aesthetic disposition of dirt; persons of contrivance who could conjure with any sort of material. As our electric-light campaign developed, a London contractor came down to put a fifteen-inch eduction-pipe through the innocent-seeming mill-dam. His imported gang came across a solid core of ancient brickwork about as workable as obsidian. They left, after using very strong words. But every other man of 'our folk' had known exactly where and what that core was, and when 'Lunnon' had sufficiently weakened it, they 'conjured' the pipe quietly through what remained.

The only thing that ever shook them was when we cut a little under the Mill foundations to fix the turbine; and found that she sat on a crib or raft of two-foot-square elm logs. What we took out, to all appearance, as untouched as when it had been put under water. Yet, in an hour, the great baulk, exposed to air, became silver dust, and the men stood round marvelling.

Although the mill building at Bateman's dates from the mid-18th century, two watermills were recorded in the parish around 1246 and it isn't far-fetched to imagine a wheel turning here back in the Conqueror's time. This short story was written in 1902, very soon after Kipling moved to his new home, and one might have expected more than a nod to traditional milling techniques. But no: Kipling pours scorn on those who refuse to move with the times – not only the the cat, the black rat and the doomed wheel within the tale itself, but, by implication, the Tory old guard and other non-progressives in the world beyond.

'Book – Book – Domesday Book!' They were letting in the water for the evening stint at Robert's Mill, and the wooden Wheel where lived the Spirit of the Mill settled to its nine-hundred-year-old song: 'Here Azor, a freeman, held one rod, but it never paid geld. *Nun-nun-nunquam geldavit.* Here Reinbert has one villein and four cottars with one plough – and wood for six hogs and two fisheries of sixpence and a mill of ten shillings – *unum molinum* – one mill. Reinbert's mill – Robert's Mill. Then and afterwards and now – *tunc et post et modo* – Robert's Mill. Book – Book – Domesday Book!'

The Bateman's mill.

'I confess,' said the Black Rat on the cross-beam, luxuriously trimming his whiskers – 'I confess I am not above appreciating my position and all it means.' He was a genuine old English black rat, a breed which, report says, is rapidly diminishing before the incursions of the brown variety.

'Appreciation is the surest sign of inadequacy,' said the Grey Cat, coiled up on a piece of sacking.

'But I know what you mean,' she added. 'To sit by right at the heart of things – eh?'

'Yes,' said the Black Rat, as the old mill shook and the heavy stones thuttered on the grist. 'To possess – er – all this environment as an integral part of one's daily life must insensibly of course . . . You see?'

'I feel,' said the Grey Cat. 'Indeed, if we are not saturated with the spirit of the Mill, who should be?'

'Book – Book – Domesday Book!' The Wheel, set to his work, was running off the tenure of the whole rape, for he knew Domesday Book backwards and forwards: '*In Ferle tenuit Abbatia de Wiltuna unam hidam et unam virgam et dimidiam. Nunquam geldavit.* And Agemond, a freeman, has half a hide and one rod. I remember Agemond well. Charmin' fellow – friend of mine. He married a Norman girl in the days when we rather looked down on the Normans as upstarts. An' Agemond's dead? So he is. Eh, dearie me! dearie me! I remember the wolves howling outside his door in the big frost of Ten Fifty-Nine . . . *Essewelde hundredum nunquam geldum reddidit.* Book! Book! Domesday Book!'

'After all,' the Grey Cat continued, 'atmosphere is life. It is the influences under which we live that count in the long run. Now, outside' – she cocked one ear towards the half-opened door – 'there is an absurd convention that rats and cats are, I won't go so far as to say natural enemies, but opposed forces. Some such ruling may be crudely effective – I don't for a minute presume to set up my standards as final – among the ditches; but from the larger point of view that one gains by living at the heart of things, it seems for a rule of life a little overstrained. Why, because some of your associates have, shall I say, liberal views on the ultimate destination of a sack of – er – middlings, don't they call them – '

'Something of that sort,' said the Black Rat, a most sharp and sweet-toothed judge of everything ground in the mill for the last three years.

'Thanks – middlings be it. *Why*, as I was saying, must I disarrange my fur and my digestion to chase you round the dusty arena whenever we happen to meet?'

'As little reason,' said the Black Rat, 'as there is for me, who, I trust, am a person of ordinarily decent instincts, to wait until you have gone on a round of calls, and then to assassinate your very charming children.'

'Exactly! It has its humorous side though.' The Grey Cat yawned. 'The miller seems afflicted by it. He shouted large and vague threats to my address, last night at tea, that he wasn't going to keep cats who 'caught no mice'. Those were his words. I remember the grammar sticking in my throat like a herring-bone.'

'And what did you do?'

'What does one do when a barbarian utters? One ceases to utter and removes. I removed – towards his pantry. It was a *riposte* he might appreciate.'

'Really those people grow absolutely insufferable,' said the Black Rat. 'There is a local ruffian who answers to the name of Mangles – a builder – who has taken possession of the outhouses on the far side of the Wheel for the last fortnight. He has constructed cubical horrors in red brick where those deliciously picturesque pigstyes used to stand. Have you noticed?'

'There has been much misdirected activity of late among the humans. They jabber inordinately. I haven't yet been able to arrive at their reason for existence.' The Cat yawned.

'A couple of them came in here last week with wires, and fixed them all about the walls. Wires protected by some abominable composition, ending in iron brackets with glass bulbs. Utterly useless for any purpose and artistically absolutely hideous. What do they mean?'

'Aaah! I have know *four*-and-twenty leaders of revolt in Faenza,' said the Cat, who kept good company with the boarders spending a summer at the Mill Farm. 'It means nothing except that humans occasionally bring their dogs with them. I object to dogs in all forms.'

'Shouldn't object to dogs,' said the Wheel sleepily . . . 'The Abbot of Wilton kept the best pack in the county. He enclosed all Harryngton Woods to Sturt Common. Aluric, a freeman, was dispossessed of his holding. They tried the case at Lewes, but he got no change out of William de Warrenne on the bench. William de Warrene fined Aluric eight and fourpence for treason, and the Abbot of Wilton excommunicated him for blasphemy. Aluric was no sportsman. Then the Abbot's brother married . . . I've forgotten her name, but she was a charmin' little woman. The Lady Philippa was her daughter. That was after the barony was conferred. She rode devilish straight to hounds. They were a bit throatier than we breed now, but a good pack: one of the best. The Abbot kept 'em in splendid shape. Now, who was the woman the Abbot kept? Book – Book! I shall have to go right back to Domesday and work up the centuries: *Modo per omnia reddit burgum tunc – tunc – tunc!* Was it *burgum* or *hundredum*? I shall remember in a minute. There's no hurry.' He paused as he turned over, silvered with showering drops.

'This won't do,' said the Waters in the sluice. 'Keep moving.'

The Wheel swung forward; the Waters roared on the buckets and dropped down to the darkness below.

'Noisier than usual,' said the Black Rat. 'It must have been raining up the valley.'

'Floods maybe,' said the Wheel dreamily. 'It isn't the proper season, but they can come without warning. I shall never forget the big one – when the Miller went to sleep and forgot to open the hatches. More than two hundred years ago it was, but I recall it distinctly. Most unsettling.'

'We lifted that wheel off his bearings,' cried the Waters. 'We said, "Take away that bauble!" And in the morning he was five miles down the valley – hung up in a tree.'

'Vulgar,' said the Cat. 'But I am sure he never lost his dignity.'

'We don't know. He looked like the Ace of Diamonds when we had finished with him . . . Move on there! Keep on moving. Over! Get over!'

'And why on this day more than any other?' said the Wheel statelily. 'I am not aware that my department requires the stimulus of external pressure to keep it up to its duties. I trust I have the elementary instincts of a gentleman.'

'Maybe,' the Waters answered together, leaping down on the buckets. 'We only know that you are very stiff on your bearings. Over! Get over!'

The Wheel creaked and groaned. There was certainly greater presssure upon him than he had ever felt, and his revolutions had increased from six and three-quarters to eight and a third per minute. But the uproar between the narrow, weed-hung walls annoyed the Grey Cat.

'Isn't it almost time,' she said plaintively, 'that the person who is paid to understand these things shuts off those vehement drippings with that screw-thing on the top of that box-thing?'

'They'll be shut off at eight o'clock as usual,' said the Rat; 'then we can go to dinner.'

'But we shan't be shut off till ever so late,' said the Waters gaily. 'We shall keep it up all night.'

'The ineradicable offensiveness of youth is partially compensated for by its eternal hopefulness,' said the Cat. 'Our dam is not, I am glad to say, designed to furnish water for more than four hours at a time. Reserve is Life.'

'Thank goodness!' said the Black Rat. 'Then they can return to their native ditches.'

'Ditches!' cried the Waters; 'Raven's Gill Brook is no ditch. It is almost navigable, and we come from there away.' They slid over solid and compact till the Wheel thudded under their weight.

'Raven's Gill Brook,' said the Rat. '*I* never heard of Raven's Gill.'

'We are the waters of Harpenden Brook – down from under Callton

Rise. Phew! How the race stinks compared with the heather country.' Another five foot of water flung itself against the Wheel, broke, roared, gurgled and was gone.

'Indeed?' said the Grey Cat. 'I am sorry to tell you that Raven's Gill Brook is cut off from this valley by an absolutely impassable range of mountains, and Callton Rise is more than nine miles away. It belongs to another system entirely.'

'Ah, yes,' said the Rat, grinning, 'but we forget that, for the young, water always runs uphill.'

'Oh, hopeless! hopeless! hopeless!' cried the Waters, descending open-palmed upon the Wheel. 'There is nothing between here and Raven's Gill Brook that a hundred yards of channelling and a few square feet of concrete could not remove; and hasn't removed!'

'And Harpenden's Brook is north of Raven's Gill and runs into Raven's Gill at the foot of Callton Rise, where the big ilex trees are, and we come from there!' These were the glassy, clear waters of the high chalk.

'And Batten's Ponds, that are fed by springs, have been led through Trott's Wood, taking the spare water from the old Witches' Spring under Churt Haw, and we – we – we are their combined waters!' Those were the Waters from the upland bogs and moors – a porter-coloured, dusky and foam-flecked flood.

'It's all very interesting,' purred the Cat to the sliding waters, 'and I have no doubt that Trott's Woods and Bott's Woods are tremendously important places; but if you could manage to do your work – whose value I don't in the least dispute – a little more soberly, I, for one, should be grateful.'

'Book – book – book – book – book – Domesday Book!' The urged Wheel was fairly clattering now: 'In Burgelstaltone a monk holds of Earl Godwin one hide and a half with eight villeins. There is a church – and a monk . . . I remember that monk. Blessed if he could rattle his rosary off any quicker than I am doing now . . . and wood for seven hogs. I must be running twelve to the minute . . . almost as fast as Steam. Damnable invention, Steam! . . . Surely it's time we went to dinner or prayers – or something. Can't keep up this pressure, day in and day out, and not feel it. I don't mind for myself, of course. *Noblesse oblige,* you know. I'm only thinking of the Upper and the Nether Millstones. They came out of the common rock. They can't be expected to – '

'Don't worry on our account, please,' said the Millstones huskily. 'So long as you supply the power we'll supply the weight and the bite.'

'Isn't it a trifle blasphemous, though, to work you in this way?' grunted the Wheel. 'I seem to remember something about the Mills of God grinding "slowly". *Slowly* was the word!'

'But we are not the Mills of God. We're only the Upper and the Nether Millstones. We have received no instructions to be anything else. We are actuated by power transmitted through you.'

'Ah, but let us be merciful as we are strong. Think of all the beautiful little plants that grow on my woodwork. There are five varieties of rare moss within less than one square yard – and all these delicate jewels of nature are being grievously knocked about by this excessive rush of the water.'

'Umph!' growled the Millstones. 'What with your religious scruples and your taste for botany we'd hardly know you for the Wheel that put the carter's son under last autumn. You never worried about *him*!'

'He ought to have known better.'

'So ought your jewels of nature. Tell 'em to grow where it's safe.'

'How a purely mercantile life debases and brutalises!' said the Cat to the Rat.

'They were such beautiful little plants too,' said the Rat tenderly. 'Maiden's-tongue and hart's-hair fern trellising all over the wall just as they do on the sides of churches in the Downs. Think what a joy the sight of them must be to our sturdy peasants pulling hay!'

'Golly!' said the Millstones. 'There's nothing like coming to the heart of things for information'; and they returned to the song that all English watermills have sung from time beyond telling:

> *There was a jovial miller once*
> *Lived on the River Dee,*
> *And this the burden of his song*
> *For ever used to be.*

Then, as fresh grist poured in and dulled the note:

> *I care for nobody – no, not I,*
> *And nobody cares for me.*

'Even these stones have absorbed something of our atmosphere,' said the Grey Cat. 'Nine-tenths of the trouble in this world comes from lack of detachment.'

'One of your people died from forgetting that, didn't he?' said the Rat.

'One only. The example has sufficed us for generations.'

'Ah! but what happened to Don't Care?' the Waters demanded.

'Brutal riding to death of the casual analogy is another mark of provincialism!' The Grey Cat raised her tufted chin. 'I am going to sleep. With my social obligations I must snatch rest when I can; but, as our old friend here says, Noblesse oblige . . . Pity me! Three functions tonight in the village, and a barn dance across the valley!'

'There's no chance, I suppose, of your looking in on the loft about two. Some of our young people are going to amuse themselves with a new sacque-dance – best white flour only,' said the Black Rat.

'I believe I am officially supposed not to countenance that sort of thing, but youth is youth . . . By the way, the humans set my milk-bowl in the loft these days; I hope your youngsters respect it.'

'My dear lady,' said the Black Rat, bowing. 'You grieve me. You hurt me inexpressibly. After all these years, too!'

'A general crush is so mixed – highways and hedges – all that sort of thing – and no one can answer for one's best friends. *I* never try. So long as mine are amusin' and in full voice, and can hold their own at a tile-party, I'm as catholic as these mixed waters in the dam here!'

'We aren't mixed. We *have* mixed. We are one now,' said the Waters sulkily.

'Still uttering?' said the Cat. 'Never mind, here's the Miller coming to shut you off. Ye-es, I have known – *four* – or five, is it? – and twenty leaders of the revolt in Faenza . . . A little more babble in the dam, a little more noise in the sluice, a little extra splashing on the wheel, and then – '

'They will find that nothing has occurred,' said the Black Rat. 'The old things persist and survive and are recognised – our old friend here first of all. By the way,' he turned towards the Wheel, 'I believe we have to congratulate you on your latest honour.'

'Profoundly well deserved – even if he had never – as he has – laboured strenuously through a long life for the amelioration of millkind,' said the Cat, who belonged to many tile and oast-house committees. 'Doubly deserved, I may say, for the silent and dignified rebuke his existence offers to the clattering, fidgety-footed demands of – er – some people. What form did the honour take?'

'It was,' said the Wheel bashfully, 'a machine-moulded pinion.'

'Pinions! Oh, how heavenly!' the Black Rat sighed. 'I never see a bat without wishing for wings.'

'Not exactly that sort of pinion,' said the Wheel, 'but a really ornate circle of toothed iron wheels. Absurd, of course, but gratifying. Mr Mangles and an associate herald invested me with it personally – on my left rim – the side that you can't see from the mill. I hadn't meant to say anything about it – or the new steel straps round my axles – bright red, you know – to be worn on all occasions – but, without false modesty, I assure you that the recognition cheered me not a little.'

'How intensely gratifying,' said the Black Rat. 'I must really steal an hour between lights some day and see what they are doing on your left side.'

'By the way, have you any light on this recent activity of Mr Mangles?'

the Grey Cat asked. 'He seems to be building small houses on the far side of the tail-race. Believe me, I don't ask from any vulgar curiosity.'

'It affects our Order,' said the Back Rat simply but firmly.

'Thank you,' said the Wheel. 'Let me see if I can tabulate it properly. Nothing like system in accounts of all kinds. Book! Book! Book! On the side of the Wheel towards the hundred of Burgelstaltone, where till now was a stye of three hogs, Mangles, a freeman, with four villeins and two carts of two thousand bricks, has a new small house of five yards and a half, and one roof of iron and a floor of cement. Then, now, and afterwards beer in large tankards. And Felden, a stranger, with three villeins and one very great cart, deposits on it one engine of iron and brass and a small iron mill of four feet, and a broad strap of leather. And Mangles, the builder, with two villeins, constructs the floor for the same, and a floor of new brick with wires for the small mill. There are there also chalices filled with iron and water, in number fifty-seven. The whole is valued at one hundred and seventy-four pounds . . . I'm sorry I can't make myself clearer, but you can see for yourself.'

'Amazingly lucid,' said the Cat. She was the more to be admired because the language of Domesday Book is not, perhaps, the clearest medium wherein to describe a small but complete electric-light intallation, deriving its power from a water-wheel by means of cogs and gearing.

'See for yourself – by all means, see for yourself,' said the Waters, spluttering and choking with mirth.

'Upon my word,' said the Black Rat furiously, 'I may be at fault, but I wholly fail to preceive where these offensive eavesdroppers – er – come in. We were discussing a matter that solely affected our Order.'

Suddenly they heard, as they had heard many times before, the Miller shutting off the water. To the rattle and rumble of the labouring stones succeeded thick silence, punctuated with little drops from the stayed wheel. Then some water-bird in the dam fluttered her wings as she slid to her nest, and the plop of a water-rat sounded like the fall of a log in the water.

'It is all over – it always is all over at just this time. Listen, the Miller is going to bed – as usual. Nothing has occurred,' said the Cat.

Something creaked in the house where the pigstyes had stood, as metal engaged on metal with a clink and a burr.

'Shall I turn her on?' cried the Miller.

'Ay,' said the voice from the dynamo-house.

'A human in Mangles' new house!' the Rat squeaked.

'What of it?' said the Grey Cat. 'Even supposing Mr Mangles' cat's-meat-coloured hovel pullulated with humans, can't you see for yourself that – ?'

There was a solid crash of released waters leaping upon the Wheel more furiously than ever, a grinding of cogs, a hum like the hum of a hornet, and then the unvisited darkness of the old mill was scattered by intolerable white light. It threw up every cobweb, every burl and knot in the beams and the floor; till the shadows behind the flakes of rough plaster on the wall lay clear-cut as shadows of mountains on the photographed moon.

'See! See! See!' hissed the Waters in full flood. 'Yes, see for yourselves. Nothing has occurred. Can't you see?'

The Rat, amazed, had fallen from his foothold and lay half-stunned on the floor. The Cat, following her instinct, leaped nigh to the ceiling, and with flattened ears and bared teeth backed in a corner ready to fight whatever terror might be loosed on her.

But nothing happened. Through the long aching minutes nothing whatever happened, and her wire-brush tail returned slowly to its proper shape.

'Whatever it is,' she said at last, 'it's overdone. They can never keep it up, you know.'

'Much you know,' said the Waters. 'Over you go, old man. You can take the full head of us now. Those new steel axle-straps of yours can stand anything. Come along, Raven's Gill, Harpenden, Callton Rise, Batten's Ponds, Witches' Springs, all together! Let's show these gentlemen how to work!'

'But – but – I thought it was a decoration. Why – why – why – it only means more work for *me*!'

'Exactly. You're to supply about sixty eight-candle lights when required. But they won't be all in use at once – '

'Ah! I thought as much,' said the Cat. 'The reaction is bound to come.'

'*And*,' said the Waters, 'you will do the ordinary work of the mill as well.'

'Impossible!' the old Wheel quivered as it drove. 'Aluric never did it – nor Azor, nor Reinbert. Not even William de Warrenne or the Papal Legate. There's no precedent for it. I tell you there's no precedent for working a wheel like this.'

'Wait a while! We're making one as fast as we can. Aluric and Co. are dead. So's the Papal Legate. You've no notion how dead they are, but we're here – the Waters of Five Separate Systems. We're just as interesting as Domesday Book. Would you like to hear about the land-tenure in Trott's Wood? It's squat-rights, chiefly.' The mocking Waters leaped one over the other, chuckling and chattering profanely.

'In that hundred Jenkins, a tinker, with one dog – *unus canis* – holds by the Grace of God and a habit he has of working hard, *unam hidam* – a large potato-patch. Charmin' fellow, Jenkins. Friend of ours. Now, who the dooce did Jenkins keep? . . . In the hundred of Callton is one charcoal-burner *irreligiosissimus homo* – a bit of a rip – but a thorough sportsman. *Ibi est ecclesia. Non multum.* Not much of a church, *quia* because, *episcopus* the Vicar irritated the Nonconformists *tunc et post et modo* – then and afterwards and now – until they built a cut-stone Congregational chapel with red brick facings that did not return itself – *defendebat se* – at four thousand pounds.'

'Charcoal-burners, vicars, schismatics, and red brick facings,' groaned the Wheel. 'But this is sheer blasphemy. What waters have they let in upon me?'

'Floods from the gutters. Faugh, this light is positively sickening!' said the Cat, rearranging her fur.

'We come down from the clouds or up from the springs, exactly like all other waters everywhere. Is that what's surprising you?' sang the Waters.

'Of course not. I know my work if you don't. What I complain of is your lack of reverence and repose. You've no instinct of deference towards your betters – your heartless parody of the Sacred volume (the Wheel meant Domesday Book) proves it.'

'Our betters?' said the Waters most solemnly. 'What is there in all this damned race that hasn't come down from the clouds, or – '

'Spare me that talk, please,' the Wheel persisted. 'You'd never understand. It's the tone – your tone that we object to.'

'Yes. It's your tone,' said the Black Rat, picking himself up limb by limb.

'If you thought a trifle more about the work you're supposed to do, and a trifle less about your precious feelings, you'd render a little more duty in return for the power vested in you – we mean wasted on you,' the Waters replied.

'I have been some hundred of years laboriously acquiring the knowledge which you see fit to challenge so light-heartedly,' the Wheel jarred.

'Challenge him! Challenge him! clamoured the little waves riddling down through the tail-race. 'As well now as later. Take him up!'

The main mass of the Waters plunging on the Wheel shocked that well-bolted structure almost into box-lids by saying: 'Very good. Tell us what you suppose yourself to be doing at the present moment.'

'Waiving the offensive form of your question, I answer, purely as a matter of courtesy, that I am engaged in the trituration of farinaceous substances whose ultimated destination it would be a breach of the trust reposed in me to reveal.'

'Fiddle!' said the Waters. 'We knew it all along! The first direct question shows his ignorance of his own job. Listen, old thing. Thanks to us, you are now actuating a machine of whose construction you know nothing, that that machine may, over wires of whose ramifications you are, by your very position, profoundly ignorant, deliver a power which you can never realise, to localities beyond the extreme limits of your mental horizon, with the object of producing phenomena which in your wildest dreams (if you ever dream) you could never comprehend. Is that clear, or would you like it all in words of four syllables?'

'Your assumptions are deliciously sweeping, but may I point out that a decent and – the dear old Abbot of Wilton would have put it in his resonant monkish Latin much better than I can – a scholarly reserve does not necessarily connote blank vacuity of mind on all subjects?'

'Ah, the dear old abbot of Wilton,' said the Rat sympathetically, as one nursed in that bosom. 'Charmin' fellow – thorough scholar and gentleman. Such a pity!'

'Oh, Sacred Fountains! – the Waters were fairly boiling. 'He goes out of his way to expose his ignorance by triple bucketfuls. He creaks to high Heaven that he is hopelessly behind the common order of things! He invites the streams of Five Watersheds to witness his su-su-supernal incompetence, and then he talks as though there were untold reserves of knowledge behind him that he is too modest to bring forward. For a bland, circular, absolutely sincere impostor, you're a miracle, O Wheel!'

'I do not pretend to be anything more than an integral portion of an accepted and not altogether mushroom institution.'

'Quite so,' said the Waters. 'Then go round – hard – '

'To what end?' asked the Wheel.

'Till a big box of tanks in your house begins to fizz and fume – gassing is the proper word.'

'It would be,' said the Cat, sniffing.

'That will show that your accumulators are full. When the accumulators are exhausted, and the lights burn badly, you will find us whacking you round and round again.'

'The end of life as decreed by Mangles and his creatures is to go whacking round and round for ever,' said the Cat.

'In order,' the Rat said, 'that you may throw raw and unnecessary illumination upon all the unloveliness in the world. Unloveliness which we shall – er – have always with us. At the same time you will riotously neglect the so-called little but vital graces that make up Life.'

'Yes, Life,' said the Cat, 'with its dim delicious half-tones and veiled indeterminate distances. Its surprisals, escapes, encounters and dizzying leaps – its full-throated choruses in honour of the morning star, and its melting reveries beneath the sun-warmed wall.'

'Oh, you can go on the tiles, Pussalina, just the same as usual,' said the laughing Waters. '*We* shan't interfere with you.'

'On the tiles, forsooth!' hissed the Cat.

'Well, that's what it amounts to,' persisted the Waters. 'We see a good deal of the minor graces of life on our way down to our job.'

'And – but I fear I speak to deaf ears – do they never impress you?' said the Wheel.

'Enormously,' said the Waters. 'We have already learned six refined synonyms for loafing.'

'But (here again I feel as though preaching in the wilderness) it never occurs to you that there may exist some small difference between the wholly animal – ah – rumination of bovine minds and the discerning, well-apportioned leisure of the finer type of intellect?'

'Oh, yes. The bovine mind goes to sleep under a hedge and makes no bones about it when it's shouted at. We've seen that – in haying time – all along the meadows. The finer type is wide awake enough to fudge up excuses for shirking, and man enough to get stuffy when its excuses aren't accepted. Turn over!'

'But, my good people, no gentleman gets stuffy as you call it. A certain proper pride, to put it no higher, forbids – '

'Nothing that he wants to do if he really wants to do it. Get along! What are you giving us? D'you suppose we've scoured half heaven in the clouds and half earth in the mists, to be taken in at this time of the day by a bone-idle, old hand-quern of your type?'

'It is not for me to bandy personalities with you. I can only say that I simply decline to accept the situation.'

'Decline away. It doesn't make any odds. They'll probably put in a turbine if you decline too much.'

'What's a turbine?' said the Wheel quickly.

'A little thing you don't see, that performs surprising revolutions. But you won't decline. You'll hang on to your two nice red-strapped axles and your new machine-mouled pinions like – a – like a leech on a lily stem! There's centuries of work in your old bones if you'd only apply yourself to it; and, mechanically, an overshot wheel with this head of water is about as efficient as a turnbine.'

'So in future I am to be considered mechanically? I have been painted by at least five Royal Academicians.'

'Oh, you can be painted by five hundred when you aren't at work, of course. But while you are at work you'll work. You won't half-stop and think and talk about rare plants and dicky-birds and farinaceous fiduciary interests. You'll continue to revolve, and this new head of water will see that you do so continue.'

'It is a matter on which it would be exceedingly ill-advised to form a hasty or a premature conclusion. I will give it my most careful consideration,' said the Wheel.

'Please do,' said the Water gravely. 'Hullo! Here's the Miller again.'

The Cat coiled herself in a picturesque attitude on the softest corner of a sack, and the Rat, without haste, yet certainly without rest, slipped behind the sacking as though an appointment had just occurred to him.

In the doorway, with the young Engineer, stood the Miller grinning amazedly.

'Well – well – well! 'tis true-ly won'erful. An' what a power o' dirt. It come over me now looking at these lights, that I've never rightly seen my own mill before. She needs a lot bein' done to her.'

'Ah! I suppose one must make onself moderately agreeable to the baser sort. They have their uses. This thing controls the dairy.' The Cat, mincing on her toes, came forward and rubbed her head against the Miller's knee.

'Ay, you pretty puss,' he said, stooping. 'You're as big a cheat as the rest of 'em that catch no mice about me. A won'erful smooth-skinned, rough-tongued cheat you be. I've more than half a mind – '

'She does her work well,' said the Engineer, pointing to where the Rat's beady eyes showed behind the sacking. 'Cats and Rats livin' together – see?'

'Too much they do – too long they've done. I'm sick and tired of if. Go and take a swim and larn to find your own vittles honest when you come out, Pussy.'

'My word!' said the Waters, as a sprawling Cat landed all unannounced in the centre of the tail-race. 'Is that you, Mewsalina? You seem to have been quarrelling with your best friend. Get over to the left. It's shallowest there. Up on that alder-root with all four paws. Good night!'

'You'll never get any they rats,' said the Miller, as the young Engineer struck wrathfully with his stick at the sacking. 'They're not the common sort. They're the old black English sort.'

'Are they, by Jove? I must catch one to stuff, some day.'

Six months later, in the chill of a January afternoon, they were letting in the Waters as usual.

'Come along! It's both gears this evening,' said the Wheel, kicking joyously in the first rush of the icy stream. 'There's a heavy load of grist just in from Lambert's Wood. Eleven miles it came in an hour and a half in our new motor lorry, and the Miller's rigged five new five-candle lights in his cow-stables. I'm feeding 'em tonight. There's a cow due to calve. Oh, while I think of it, what's the news from Callton Rise?'

'The waters are finding their level as usual – but why do you ask?' said the deep outpouring Waters.

'Because Mangles and Felden and the Miller are talking of increasing the plant here and running a saw-mill by electricity. I was wondering whether we – '

'I beg your pardon,' said the Waters, chuckling. '*What* did you say?'

'Whether *we*, of course, had power enough for the job. It will be a biggish contract. There's all Harpenden Brook to be considered and Batten's Ponds as well, and Witches' Spring, and the Churt Haw system.'

'We've power enough for anything in the world,' said the Waters. 'The only question is whether you could stand the strain if we came down on you full head.'

'Of course I can,' said the Wheel. 'Mangles is going to turn me into a set of turbines – beauties.'

'Oh – er – I suppose it's the frost that has made us a little thick-headed, but to whom are we talking?' asked the amazed Waters.

'To me – the Spirit of the Mill, of course.'

'Not to the old Wheel, then?'

'I happen to be living in the old Wheel just at present. When the turbines are installed I shall go and live in them. What earthly difference does it make?'

'Absolutely none,' said the Waters, 'in the earth or in the waters under the earth. But we thought turbines didn't appeal to you.'

'Not like turbines? Me? My dear fellows, turbines are good for fifteen hundred revolutions a minute – and with our power we can drive 'em at full speed. Why, there's nothing we couldn't grind or saw or illuminate or heat with a set of turbines! That's to say if all the Five Watersheds are agreeable.'

'Oh, we've been agreeable for ever so long.'

'Then why didn't you tell me?'

'Don't know. Suppose it slipped our memory.' The Waters were holding themselves in for fear of bursting with mirth.

'How careless of you! You should keep abreast of the age, my dear fellows. We might have settled it long ago, if you'd only spoken. Yes, four good turbines and a neat brick penstock – eh? This old Wheel's absurdly out of date.'

'Well,' said the Cat, who after a little proud seclusion had returned to her place impenitent as ever. 'Praised be Pasht and the Old Gods, that whatever may have happened *I*, at least have preserved the Spirit of the Mill!'

She looked round as expecting her faithful ally, the Black Rat; but that every week the Engineer had caught and stuffed him, and had put him in a glass case; he being a genuine old English black rat. That breed, the report says, is rapidly diminishing before the incursions of the brown variety.

FARCE, FRAUD AND PHILANTHROPY

From 'Something of Myself'

For rest and refreshment and dearly-loved experiments and anxieties, during the six months or so of each year that we stayed in England, there was always the House and the land, and on occasion the Brook at the foot of our garden, which would flood devastatingly. As she supplied the water for our turbine, and as the little weir which turned her current into the little mill-race was of a frail antiquity, one had to attend to her often and at once, and always at the most inconvenient moment.

Undiscerning folks would ask: 'What do you find to do in the country?' Our answer was: 'Everything except time to do it.'

We began with tenants – two or three small farmers on our very few acres – from whom we learned that farming was a mixture of farce, fraud, and philanthropy that stole the heart out of the land. After many, and some comic experiences, we fell back on our own county's cattle – the big, red Sussex breed who make beef and not milk. One got something at least for one's money from the mere sight of them, and they did not tell lies. Rider Haggard would visit us from time to time and give of his ample

The Dudwell stream in gentle mood.

land-wisdom. I remember I planted some new apple-trees in an old orchard then rented by an Irishman, who at once put in an agile and hungry goat. Haggard met the combination suddenly one morning. He had gifts of speech, and said very clearly indeed that one might as well put Satan in an orchard as a goat. I forget what – though I acted on it – he said about tenants. His comings were always a joy to us and the children, who followed him like hounds in the hope of 'more South African stories'. Never was a better tale-teller or, to my mind, a man with a more convincing imagination. We found by accident that each could work at ease in the other's company. So he would visit me, and I him, with work in hand: and between us we could even hatch out tales together – a most exacting test of sympathy.

THE STUDY

Writers' workrooms can often disappoint, but Kipling's study at Bateman's is much as he left it – even to several of the objects mentioned below.

From 'Something of Myself'

And with what tools did I work in my own mould-loft? I had always been choice, not to say coquettish in this respect. In Lahore for my *Plain Tales* I used a slim, octagonal-sided, agate penholder with a Waverley nib. It was a gift, and when in an evil hour it snapped I was much disturbed. Then followed a procession of impersonal hirelings each with a Waverley, and next a silver penholder with a quill-like curve, which promised well but did not perform. In Villiers Street I got me an outsize office pewter ink-pot, on which I would gouge the names of the tales and books I wrote out of it. But the housemaids of married life polished those titles away till they grew as faded as a palimpsest.

I then abandoned hand-dipped Waverleys – a nib I never changed – and for years wallowed in the pin-pointed 'stylo' and its successor the 'fountain' which for me meant geyser-pens. In later years I clung to a slim, smooth, black treasure (Jael was her office name) which I picked up in Jerusalem. I tried pump-pens with glass insides, but they were of 'intolerable entrails'.

For my ink I demanded the blackest, and had I been in my Father's house, as once I was, would have kept an ink-boy to grind me Indian-ink. All 'blue-blacks' were an abomination to my Daemon, and I never found a bottled vermilion fit to rubricate initials when one hung in the wind waiting.

My writing-blocks were built for me to an unchanged pattern of large, off-white, blue sheets, of which I was most wasteful. All this old-maiderie did not prevent me when abroad from buying and using blocks, and tackle, in any country.

With a lead pencil I ceased to express – probably because I had to use a pencil in reporting. I took very few notes except of names, dates and addresses. If a thing didn't stay in my memory, I argued it was hardly worth writing out. But each man has his own method. I rudely drew what I wanted to remember.

Like most men who ply one trade in one place for any while, I always kept certain gadgets on my work-table, which was ten feet long from North to South and badly congested. One was a long, lacquer, canoe-shaped pen-tray full of brushes and dead 'fountains'; a wooden box held clips and bands; another, a tin one, pins; yet another, a bottle-slider, kept all manner of unneeded essentials from emery-paper to small screwdrivers; a paper-weight, said to have been Warren Hastings'; a tiny, weighted fur-seal and a leather crocodile sat on some of the papers; an inky foot-rule and a Father of Penwipers which a much-loved housemaid of ours presented yearly, made up the main-guard of these little fetishes.

Kipling' wrote in his book-lined study on the first floor of the house.

My treatment of books, which I looked upon as tools of my trade, was popularly regarded as barbarian. Yet I economised on my multitudinous penknives, and it did no harm to my fore-finger. There were books which I respected, because they were put in locked cases. The others, all the house over, took their chances.

Left and right of the table were two big globes, on one of which a great airman had once outlined in white paint those air-routes to the East and Australia which were well in use before my death.

FLOODING

Letter to his son John, October 28, 1909

It has been a gay and hectic week! When I left my father's house on Tuesday at 10 a.m. it was raining awfully: and it never stopped for an instant all the way. One hundred and twenty-eight miles of motoring in a downpour that wetted everything to the skin. The motor came back to Bateman's one solid clot of mud. Well! that was only the beginning of the fun! I had an idea we should have a bit of a flood in the valley but I had no notion that we should have the worst flood since 1852! Miss Coates came over at 7 p.m. on Tuesday night. She said the brook was pretty well up to the bridge. It was raining hard. At 8 o'clock it was out over the banks. By nine our square pond had backed up and was all across the lower lawn. The tennis court had been flooded long ago. By eleven o'clock the water was over a foot deep by the limes. I went out in my rubber boots to see. By midnight the water was at the south door of Bateman's – lying in one level sheet right across the garden. Then Mother and I rolled up the carpets in the hall and the drawing-room for fear it should come into the house. It was very odd to see only half the yew hedges sticking up in the moonlight. At 1 o'clock I went into the kitchen to get something to eat. I opened the cellar door and this is what I saw! Bottles and eggs and apples floating about in a foot of water. Well, it didn't seem to be much good hanging about so we went to bed and in the morning the water had gone off the lawns and we put on our rubber boots and began to take stock of the damage. Here is a little of it:

1 Dynamo by the mill flooded out and made useless.

2 Little footbridge across to Cedar Island undermined.

3 Fence of the field by the mignonette path laid down flat. The flood was within a few inches of the top of the iron fence.

4 All my bee-hives swept away from Cedar Island – with the tables they stood on. Nothing left except the top of one hive.

5 The path by the brook all knocked to bits and the brick ballast that it was made of blown across the fields.

6 One teak seat carried off and set down among the roses by the pond. The other seat floated over among the laurels.

7 The sand road knocked to pieces along its whole length.

'Well,' thinks I, 'this is gay. I wonder what has happened at Dudwell.' I went over and found that two feet of water had swept through the house in the night! Mrs Whybarn was in an awful state. All the floor was covered with fine mud. I went up to the village and bought a broom and Colonel Feilden came down with me. The Whybarn's pig had been floated out of his stye and was running about very clean and washed and very hungry. Colonel Feilden scrubbed his back with the broom which so delighted the pig that he followed Colonel Feilden all about like a dog and kept rushing at his leg in a loving fashion. So the Colonel had to smite him on the nose with the broom handle. You never saw anything so funny.

It came on to rain again yesterday and we couldn't go out. I don't know yet the full extent of the damage but I have marked the highest places to which the flood rose. You won't believe it when you see it. It rose six inches above the bottom of the mill door. It was waist deep on the tennis court!

Kipling was good at voices in a wide range of registers, so it's not surprising to find him capturing the essence of his local Sussex dialect in this short story, written in 1914. That said, there is some unevenness in its representation, and readers familiar with the Rev W.D. Parish's 'Dictionary of the Sussex Dialect', first published in 1875, will detect signs that a copy lay open on his desk. A flood features not only in this tale, but in another Sussex-based story from the same period, 'My Son's Wife'.

The valley was so choked with fog that one could scarcely see a cow's length across a field. Every blade, twig, bracken-frond and hoof-print carried water, and the air was filled with the noise of rushing ditches and field-drains, all delivering to the brook below. A week's November rain on water-logged land had gorged her to full flood, and she proclaimed it aloud.

Two men in sackcloth aprons were considering an untrimmed hedge that ran down the hillside and disappeared into mist beside those

The innocent looking Dudwell has often flooded dramatically.

roarings. They stood back and took stock of the neglected growth, tapped an elbow of hedge-oak here, a mossed beech-stub there, swayed a stooled ash back and forth, and looked at each other.

'I reckon she's about two rod thick,' said Jabez the younger, 'an' she hasn't felt iron since – when has she, Jesse?'

'Call it twenty-five year, Jabez, an' you won't be far out.'

'Umm!' Jabez rubbed his wet handbill on his wetter coat-sleeve. 'She ain't a hedge. She's all manner o' trees. We'll just about have to – ' He paused, as professional etiquette required.

'Just about have to side her up an' see what she'll bear. But hadn't we best – ' Jesse paused in his turn, both men being artists and equals.

'Get some kind o' line to go by.' Jabez ranged up and down till he found a thinner place, and with clean snicks of the handbill revealed the original face of the fence. Jesse took over the dripping stuff as it fell forward and, with a grasp and a kick, made it to lie orderly on the bank till it should be faggoted.

By noon a length of unclean jungle had turned itself into a cattle-proof barrier, tufted here and there with little plumes of the sacred holly which no woodman touches without orders.

'Now we've a witness-board to go by!' said Jesse at last.

'She won't be as easy as this all along,' Jabez answered. 'She'll need plenty stakes and binders when we come to the brook.'

'Well, ain't we plenty?' Jesse pointed to the ragged perspective ahead of them that plunged downhill into the fog. 'I lay there's a cord an' a half o' firewood, let alone faggots, 'fore we get anywhere anigh the brook.'

'The brook's got up a piece since morning,' said Jabez. 'Sounds like's if she was over Wickenden's door-stones.'

Jesse listened, too. There was a growl in the brook's roar as though she worried something hard.

'Yes. She's over Wickenden's door-stones,' he replied. 'Now she'll flood acrost Alder Bay an' that'll ease her.'

'She won't ease Jim Wickenden's hay none if she do,' Jabez grunted. 'I told Jim he'd set that liddle hay-stack o' his too low down in the medder. I told him so when he was drawin' the bottom for it.'

'I told him so, too,' said Jesse. 'I told him 'fore ever you did. I told him when the County Council tarred the roads up along.' He pointed up-hill, where unseen automobiles and road-engines droned past continually. 'A tarred road, she shoots every drop o' water into a valley same's a slate roof. 'Tisn't as'twas in the old days, when the waters soaked in and soaked out in the way o' nature. It rooshes off they tarred roads all of a lump, and naturally every drop is bound to descend into the valley. And there's tar roads both two sides this valley for ten mile. That's what I told

Jim Wickenden when they tarred the roads last year. But he's a valley man. He don't hardly ever journey up-hill.'

'What did he say when you told him that?' Jabez demanded, with a little change of voice.

'Why? What did he say to you when you told him?' was the answer.

'What he said to you, I reckon, Jesse.'

'Then you don't need me to say it over again, Jabez.'

'Well, let be how 'twill, what was he gettin' *after* when he said what he said to me?' Jabez insisted.

'*I* dunno; unless you tell me what manner o' words he said to you.'

Jabez drew back from the hedge – all hedges are nests of treachery and eavesdropping – and moved to an open cattle-lodge in the centre of the field.

'No need to go ferretin' around,' said Jesse. 'None can't see us here 'fore we see them.'

'What was Jim Wickenden gettin' at when I said he'd set his stack too near anigh the brook?' Jabez dropped his voice. 'He was in his mind.'

'He ain't never been out of it yet to my knowledge,' Jesse drawled, and uncorked his tea-bottle.

'But then Jim says: "I ain't goin' to shift my stack a yard,", he says. "The Brook's been good friends to me, and if she be minded," he says, "to take a snatch at my hay, I ain't settin' out to withstand her." That's what Jim Wickenden says to me last – last June-end 'twas,' said Jabez.

'Nor he hasn't shifted his stack, neither,' Jesse replied. 'An' if there's more rain, the brook she'll shift it for him.'

'No need to tell me! But I want to know what Jim was gettin' at!'

Jabez opened his clasp-knife very deliberately; Jesse as carefully opened his. They unfolded the newspapers that wrapped their dinners, coiled away and pocketed the string that bound the packages and sat down on the edge of the lodge manger. The rain began to fall again through the fog, and the brook's voice rose.

'But I always allowed Mary was his lawful child, like,' said Jabez, after Jesse had spoken for a while.

'"Tain't so . . . Jim Wickenden's woman she never made nothing. She come out o' Lewes with her stockin's round her heels, an' she never made nor mended aught till she died. *He* had to light fire an' get breakfast every mornin' except Sundays, while she sowed it abed. Then she took an' died, sixteen, seventeen, year back; but she never had no children.'

'They was valley-folk,' said Jabez apologetically. 'I'd no call to go in among 'em, but I always allowed Mary – '

'No. Mary come out o' one o' those Lunnon Childern Societies. After his woman died, Jim got his mother back from his sister over to Peasmarsh, which she'd gone to house with when Jim married. His mother kept house for Jim after his woman died. They do say 'twas his mother led him on toward adoptin' of Mary – to furnish out the house with a child, like, and to keep him off of gettin' a noo woman. He mostly done what his mother contrived. 'Cardenly, twixt 'em, they asked for a child from one o' those Lunnon societies – same as it might ha' been these Barnardo children – an' Mary was sent down to 'em, in a candle-box, I've heard.'

'Then Mary is chance-born. I never knowed that,' Jabez. 'Yet I must ha' heard it some time or other . . .'

'No. She ain't. 'Twould ha' been better for some folk if she had been. She come to Jim in a candle-box with all the proper papers – lawful child o' some couple in Lunnon somewheres – mother dead, father drinkin'. *And* there was that Lunnon society's five shillin's a week for her. Jim's mother she wouldn't despise week-end money, but I never heard Jim was much of a muck-grubber. Let be how 'twill, they two mothered up Mary no bounds till it looked at last like they'd forgot she wasn't their own flesh an' blood. Yes, I reckon they forgot Mary wasn't their'n by rights.'

'That's no new thing,' said Jabez. 'There's more'n one or two in this parish wouldn't surrender back their Bernarders. You ask Mark Copley an' his woman an' that Bernarder cripple-babe o' theirs.'

'Maybe they need the five shillin',' Jesse suggested.

'It's handy,' said Jabez. 'But the child's more. "Dada" he says, an' "Mumma" he says, with his great rollin' head-piece all hurdled up in that iron collar. *He* won't live long – his backbone's rotten, like. But they Copleys do just about set store by him – five bob or no five bob.'

'Same way with Jim an' his mother,' Jesse went on. 'There was talk betwixt 'em after a few years o' not takin' any more week-end money for Mary; but let alone she never passed a farden in the mire 'thout longin's, Jim didn't care, like, to push himself forward into the Society's remembrance. So naun came of it. The week-end money would ha' made no odds to Jim – not after his uncle willed him they four cottages at Eastbourne an' money in the bank.'

'That was true, too, then? I heard something in a scadderin' word-o'-mouth way,' said Jabez.

'I'll answer for the house property, because Jim he requested my signed name at the foot o' some papers concernin' it. Regardin' the money in the bank, he nature-ally wouldn't like such things talked about all round the parish, so he took strangers for witnesses.'

'Then 'twill make Mary worth seekin' after?'

'She'll need it. Her Maker ain't done much for her outside nor yet in.'

'That ain't no odds.' Jabez shook his head till the water showered off his hat-brim. 'If Mary has money, she'll be wed before any likely pore maid. She's cause to be grateful to Jim.'

'She hides it middlin' close, then,' said Jesse. 'It don't sometimes look to me as if Mary has her natural rightful feelin's. She don't put on an apron o' Mondays 'thout being druv to it – in the kitchen or the hen-house. She's studyin' to be a school-teacher. She'll make a beauty! I never knowed her show any sort o' kindness to nobody – not even when Jim's mother was took dumb. No! 'Twadn't no stroke. It stifled the old lady in the throat here. First she couldn't shape her words no shape; then she clucked, Ñke, an' lastly he couldn't more than suck down spoon-meat an' hold her peace. Jim took her to Doctor Harding, an' Harding he bundled her off to Brighton Hospital on a ticket, but they couldn't make no stay to her afflictions there; and she was bundled off to Lunnon, an' they lit a great old lamp inside her, and Jim told me they couldn't make out nothing in no sort there; and, along o' one thing an' another, an' all their spyin's and pryin's, she come back a hem sight worse than when she started. Jim said he'd have no more hospitalisin', so he give her a slate, which she tied to her waist-string, and what she was minded to say she writ on it.'

'Now, I never knowed that! But they're valley-folk,' Jabez repeated.

''Twadn't particular noticeable, for she wasn't a talkin' woman any time o' her days. Mary had all three's tongue . . . Well, then, two years this summer, come what I'm tellin' you. Mary's Lunnon father, which they'd put clean out of their minds, arrived down from Lunnon with the law on his side, sayin' he'd take his daughter back to Lunnon after all. I was working for Mus' Dockett at Pounds Farm that summer, but I was obligin' Jim that evenin' muckin' out his pig-pens. I seed a stranger come traipsin' over the bridge agin' Wickenden's door-stones. 'Twadn't the new County Council bridge with the handrail. They hadn't given it in for a public right o' way then. 'Twas just a bit o' lathy old plank which Jim had throwed acrost the book for his own conveniences. The man wasn't drunk – only a little concerned in liquor, like – an' his back was a mask where he'd slipped in the muck comin' along. He went up the bricks past Jim's mother, which was feedin' the ducks, an' set himself down at the table inside – Jim was just changin' his socks – an' the man let Jim know all his rights and aims regardin' Mary. Then there just about was a hurly-bulloo! Jim's fust mind was to pitch him forth, but he'd done that once in his young days and got six months up to Lewes jail along o' the man fallin' on his head. So he swallowed his spittle an' let him talk. The law about Mary was on the man's side from fust to last, for he showed us all the papers. Then Mary come downstairs – she'd been studyin' for an examination – an' the man tells her who he was, an' she says he had ought to have took proper care of his own flesh and blood while he had it by him, an' not to think he could ree-claim it when it suited. He says somethin' or other, but she looks him up an' down, front an' backwent, an' she just tongues him scadderin' out o' doors, and he went away stuffin' all the papers back into his hat, talkin' most abusefully. Then se come back an' freed her mind aginst Jim an' his mother for not havin' warned her of her upbringin's, which it come out she hadn't ever been told. They didn't say naun to her. They never did. *I'd* ha' packed her off with any man that would ha' took her – an' God's pity on him!'

'Umm!' said Jabez, and sucked his pipe.

'So then, that was the beginnin'. The man come back again next week or so, an' he catched Jim alone, 'thout his mother this time, an' he fair beazled him with his papers an' his talk – for the law was on his side – till Jim went down into his money-purse an' give him ten shillings hush-money – he told me – to withdraw away for a bit an' leave Mary with 'em.'

'But that's no way to get rid o' man or woman,' Jabez said.

'No more 'tis. I told Jim so. "What can I do?" Jim says. "That law's *with* the man. I walk about daytimes thinkin' o' it till I sweats my underclothes ringin', an' I lie abed nights think' o' it till I sweats my sheets all of a sop. 'Tisn't as if I was a young man," he says, "nor yet as if I was a pore man. Maybe he'll drink hisself to death." I e'en a'most told him outright what foolishness he was enterin' into, but he knowed it – he knowed it – because he said next time the man come 'twould be fifteen shillin's. An' next time 'twas. Just fifteen shillin's!'

'An' was the man her father?' asked Jabez.

'He had the proofs an' the papers. Jim showed me what that Lunnon Childern's Society had answered when Mary writ up to 'em an' taxed 'em with it. I lay she hadn't been proper polite in her letters to 'em, for they answered middlin' short. They said the matter was out o' their hands, but – let's see if I remember – oh, yes – they ree-gretted there had been an oversight. I reckon they had sent Mary out in the candle-box as a orphan instead o' havin' a father. Terrible awkward! Then, when he'd drinked up the money, the man come again – in his usuals – an' he kept hammerin' on and hammerin' on about his duty to his pore dear wife, an' what he'd do for his dear daughter in Lunnon, till the tears runned down his two dirty cheeks an' he come away with more money. Jim used to slip it into his hand behind the door; but his mother she heard the chink. She didn't hold with hush-money. She'd write out all her feelin's on the slate, an' Jim 'ud be settin' up half the night answerin' back an' showing that the man had the law with him.'

'Hadn't that man no trade nor business, then?'

'He told me he was a printer. I reckon, though, he lived on the rates like the rest of 'em up there in Lunnon.'

'An' how did Mary take it?'

'She said she'd sooner go into service than go with the man. I reckon a mistress 'ud be middlin' put to it for a maid 'fore she put Mary into cap an' gown. She wass studyin' to be a schoo-oo-l teacher. A beauty she'll make . . .

'Well, that was how things went that fall. Mary's Lunnon father kep' comin' an' comin' 'carden as he'd drinked out the money Jim gave him; an' each time he'd put up his price for not takin' Mary away. Jim's mother, she didn't like partin' with no money, an' bein' obliged to write her feelin's on the slate instead of givin' 'em vent by mouth, she was just about mad. Just about she *was* mad!

'Come November I lodged with Jim in the outside room over 'gainst his hen-house. I paid *her* my rent. I was workin' for Docket at Pounds – gettin' chestnut-bats out o' Perry Shaw. Just such weather as this be – rain atop o' rain after a wet October. (An' I remember it ended in dry frostes right away up to Christmas.) Dockett he'd sent up to Perry Shaw for me – no, he comes puffin' up to me himself – because a big corner-piece o' the bank had slipped into the brook where she makes that elber at the bottom o' the Seventeen Acre, an' all the rubbishy alders an' sallies which he ought to have cut out when he took the farm, they'd slipped with the slip, an' the brook was comin' rooshin' down atop of 'em, an' they'd just about back an' spill the waters over his winter wheat. The water was lyin' in the flats already. "Gor a-mighty, Jesse!" he bellers out at me, "get that rubbish away all manners you can. Don't stop for no faggotin', but give the brook play or my wheat's past salvation. I can't lend you no help," he says, "But work an' I'll pay ye." '

'You had him there,' Jabez chuckled.

'Yes. I reckon I had ought to have drove my bargain, but the brook was backin' up on the good bread-corn. So 'cardenly, I laid into the mess of it, workin' off the bank where the trees was drownin' themselves head-down in the roosh – just such weather as this – an' the brook creepin' up on me all the time. 'Long towards noon, Jim comes mowchin' along with his toppin' axe over his shoulder.

'"Be you minded for an extra hand at your job?" he says.

'"Be you minded to turn to?" I ses, an' – no more talk to it – Jim laid in alongside o' me. He's no bunger with a toppin' axe.'

'Maybe, but I've seed him at a job o' throwin' in the woods, an' he didn't seem to make out no shape,' said Jabez. 'He haven't got the shoulders, nor yet the judgement – *my* opinion – when he's dealin' with full-girth timber. He don't rightly make up his mind where he's goin' to throw her.'

'We wasn't throwin' nothin'. We was cuttin' out they soft alders, an' haulin' 'em up the bank 'fore they could back the waters on the wheat. Jim didn't say much, 'less it was that he'd had a post-card from Mary's Lunnon father, night before, sayin' he was comin' down that mornin'. Jim, he'd sweated all night, an' he didn't reckon hisself equal to the talkin' an' the swearin' an' the cryin', an' his mother blamin' him afterwards on the slate. "It spiled my day to think of it," he ses, when we was eatin' our pieces. "So I've fair cried dunghill an' run. Mother'll have to tackle him by hersself. I lay she won't give him no hush-money,' he ses. "I lay he'll be surprised by the time he's done with *her*," he ses. An' that was e'en a'most all the talk we had concernin' it. But he's no bunger with the toppin' axe.

'The brook she'd crep up an' up on us, an' she kep' creepin' upon us till we was workin' knee-deep in the shallers, cuttin' an' pookin' an' pullin' what we could get o' the rubbish. There was a middlin' lot comin' down-stream, too – cattle-bars an' hop-poles and odds-ends bats, all poltin' down together; but they rooshed round the elber good shape by the time we'd backed out they drowned trees. Come four o'clock we reckoned we'd done a proper day's work, an' she'd take no harm if we left her.

'We couldn't puddle about there in the dark an' wet to no more advantage. Jim he was pourin' the water out of his boots – no, I was doin' that. Jim was kneelin' to unlace his'n. "Damn it all, Jesse," he ses, standin'' up; "the flood must be over my doorsteps at home, for here comes my old white-top bee-skep!"'

'Yes. I allus heard he paints his beek-skeps,' Jabez put in. 'I dunno paint don't tarrify bees more'n it keeps 'em dry.'

' "I'll have a pook at it," he ses, an' he pooks at it as it comes round the elber. The roosh nigh jerked the pooker out of his hand-grips, an' he calls to me, an' I come runnin' barefoot. Then we pulled on the pooker, an' it reared up on eend in the roosh, an' we guessed what 'twas. 'Cardenly we pulled it in into a shaller, an' it rolled a piece, an' a great old stiff man's arm nigh hit me in the face. Then we was sure. "'Tis a man," ses Jim. But the face was all a mask. "I reckon it's Mary's Lunnon father," he ses presently. "Lend me a match and I'll make sure." He never used baccy. We lit three matches one by another, well's we could in the rain, an' he cleaned off some o' the slob with a tussick o' grass. "Yes," he ses. "It's Mary's Lunnon father. He won't tarrify us no more. D'you want him, Jesse?" he ses.

' "No," I ses. "If this was Eastbourne beach like, he'd be half-a-crown apiece to us 'fore the coroner; but now we'd only lose a day havin' to 'tend the inquest. I lay he fell into the brook."

' "I lay he did," says Jim. "I wonder if he saw mother." He turns him over, an' opens his coat and puts his fingers in the waistcoat pocket an' starts laughin'. "He's seen mother, right enough," he ses. "An' he's got the best of her, too. *She* won't be able to crow no more over me 'bout givin' him money. *I* never give him more than a sovereign. She's give him two!"an' he trousers 'em, laughin' all the time. "An' now we'll pook him back again, for I've done with him," he ses.

'So we pooked him back into the middle of the brook, an' we saw he went round the elber 'thout balkin', an' we walked quite a piece beside of him to set him on his ways. When we couldn't see no more, we went home by the high road, because we knowed the brook 'u'd be out acrost the medders, an' we wasn't gooin' to hunt for Jim's little rotten old bridge in that dark – an' rainin' Heavens' hard, too. I was middlin' pleased to see light an' vittles again when we got home. Jim he pressed me to come insides for a drink. He don't drink in a generality, but he was rid of all his troubles that evenin', d'ye see? "Mother," he ses so soon as the door ope'd, "have you seen him?" She whips out her slate an' writes down – "No." "Oh, no," ses Jim. "You don't get out of it that way, mother. I lay you *have* seen him, an' I lay he's bested you for all your talk, same as he bested me. Make a clean breast of it, mother," he ses. "He got round you too." She was goin' for the slate again, but he stops her. "It's all right, mother," he ses. "I've seen him sense you have, an' he won't trouble us no more." The old lady looks up quick as a robin, an' she writes, "Did he say so?" "No,' ses Jim laughin'. "He didn't say so. That's how I know. But he bested you, mother. You can't have it in at *me* for bein' soft-hearted. You're twice as tender-hearted as what I be. Look!" he ses, an' he shows her the two sovereigns. "Put 'em away where they belong," he ses. "He won't never come for no more; an' now we'll have our drink,' he ses, "for we've earned it."

"Nature-ally they weren't goin' to let me see where they kep' their monies. She went upstairs with it – for the whisky.'

'I never knowed Jim was a drinkin' man – in his own house, like,' said Jabez.

'No more he isn't; but what he takes he likes good. He won't tech no publican's hogwash acrost the bar. Four shillin's he paid for that bottle o' whisky. I know, because when the old lady brought it down there wasn't more'n jest a liddle few dreenin's an' dregs in it. Nothin' to set before neighbours, I do assure you.'

' "Why, 'twas half full last week, mother,' he ses. "You don't mean," he ses, "you've given him all that as well? It's two shillin's worth," he ses.

(That's how I knowed he paid four.) "Well, well, mother, you be too tender-'earted to live. But I don't grudge it to him," he ses. "I don't grudge him nothin' he can keep." So, 'cardenly, we drinked up what little sup was left.'

'An' what come to Mary's Lunnun father?' said Jabez, after a full minute's silence.

'I be too tired to go readin' papers of evenin's; but Dockett he told me, that very week, I think, that they'd inquested on a man down at Robertsbridge which had polted and polted up agin' so many bridges an' banks, like, they couldn't make naun out of him.'

'An' what did Mary say to all these doin's?'

'The old lady bundled her off to the village 'fore her Lunnon father come, to buy weekend stuff (an' she fogot the half o' it). When we come in she was upstairs studyin' to be a school-teacher. None told her naun about it. 'Twadn't girls' affairs.'

'Reckon she knowed?' Jabez went on.

'She? She must have guessed it middlin' close when she saw her money come back. But she never mentioned it in writing so far's I know. She were more worrited that night on account of two-three her chickens bein' drowned, for the flood had skewed their old hen-house round on her postes. I cobbled her up next mornin' when the brook shrinked.'

'An' where did you find the bridge? Some fur dowstream, didn't ye?'

'Just where she allus was. She hadn't shifted but very little. The brook had gulled out the bank a piece under one eends of the plank, so's she was liable to tilt ye sideways if you wasn't careful. But I pooked three-four bricks under her, an' she was all plumb again.'

'Well, I dunno how it _looks_ like, but let be how 'twill,' said Jabez, 'he hadn't no business to come down from Lunnon tarrifyin' people, an' threatenin' to take away children which they'd hobbed up for their lawful own – even if 'twas Mary Wickenden.'

'He had the business right enough, an' he had the law with him – not gettin' over that,' said Jesse. 'But he had the drink with him, too, an' that was where he failed, like.'

'Well, well! Let be how 'twill, the brook was a good friend to Jim. I see it now. I allus _did_ wonder what he was gettin' at when he said that, when I talked to him about shiftin' the stack. "You dunno everythin'," he ses. "The Brook's been a good friend to me," he ses, "an' if she's minded to have a snatch at my hay, _I_ ain't settin' out to withstand her." '

'I reckon she's about shifted it, too, by now,' Jesse chuckled. 'Hark! That ain't any slip off the bank which she's got hold of.'

The Brook had changed her note again. It sounded as though she were mumbling something soft.

Kipling enjoyed the role of country squire, and closely observed the finer points of the various jobs carried out by the people in his employ. His poem in praise of gardeners, although it has no obvious Sussex reference, was clearly based on watching the tending of his own estate.

As this letter shows, he liked to 'get stuck in' himself from time to time.

Letter to Andrew Macphail, June 25, 1910

A mad week climatically. We were out in the motor mostly. Got a storm at Guildford, several at Oxford and the tail of one at Reading and came home to find there had been a true western cloudburst in the wood behind where we found the wired rabbit [on a previous visit]. The spilth of it came down the little brook that runs at right angles to our own (it's so small you never saw it) knocked over fences, smashed hedges and gouged out fifty yards of my poor long-suffering road even to the bones of it. So three men for two weeks have hardly made good what that burst did in two hours, and a mile and a half away there was nothing more than gentle rain! Then followed divine weather – fat, lazy June heat and

Pergola and greenhouse at Bateman's.

the hay so prosperous I went and cut three acres of it. The Gods heard and – not to be too refined – pissed on it without break for the last three days. My hay I think will not be good but I have given great joy to my conservative farmers who have not yet put their machines to work. They have almost a bestial instinct what the weather will be. I tried to be progressive. There is no moral.

Yesterday (these are the things one really works for) the wife and I had a glorious day in the garden alone . . . building a little dry stone wall to the edge of a bed which had long been an eyesore. We knocked off, stiff, sore (stones aren't easy to handle), pretty dirty, but quite happy. Why is it one gets more joy over a job like that than 'literature'? And also, we've been filling up holes and weak places along the river with spiles and dirt and building retaining walls to the face of a cess-pit; and I've

sown some buckwheat and our hollies are growing and we feel that this year marks great things in the garden. It's like a state – a garden. Comes a time when for no obvious reason everything shows and a few dollars tell more on the surface than hundreds did in the time of construction.

One of the gardeners' sheds at Bateman's today.

The Glory of the Garden

Our England is a garden that is full of stately views,
Of borders, beds and shrubberies and lawns and avenues,
With statues on the terraces and peacocks strutting by;
But the Glory of the Garden lies in more than meets the eye.

For where the old thick laurels grow, along the thin red wall,
You will find the tool- and potting-sheds which are the heart of all;
The cold-frames and the hot-houses, the dungpits and the tanks,
The rollers, carts and drainpipes, with the barrows and the planks.

And there you'll see the gardeners, the men and 'prentice boys
Told off to do as they are bid and do it without noise;
For, except when seeds are planted and we shout to scare the birds,
The Glory of the Garden it abideth not in words.

And some can pot begonias and some can bud a rose,
And some are hardly fit to trust with anything that grows;
But they can roll and trim the lawns and sift the sand and loam,
For the Glory of the Garden occupieth all who come.

Our England is a garden, and such gardens are not made
By singing 'Oh, how beautiful!' and sitting in the shade,
While better men than we go out and start their working lives
At grubbing weeds from gravel-paths with broken dinner-knives.

There's not a pair of legs so thin, there's not a head so thick,
There's not a hand so weak and white, nor yet a heart so sick,
But it can find some needful job that's crying to be done,
For the Glory of the Garden glorifieth every one.

Then seek your job with thankfulness and work till further orders,
If it's only netting strawberries or killing slugs on borders;
And when your back stops aching and your hands begin to harden,
You will find yourself a partner in the Glory of the Garden.

Oh, Adam was a gardener, and God who made him sees
That half a proper gardener's work is done upon his knees,
So when your work is finished, you can wash your hands and pray
For the Glory of the Garden, that it may not pass away!
And the Glory of the Garden it shall never pass away!

THE CUCKOO

The 'Heffle Fair' was established in 1315 and was still flourishing every April 14 in Kipling's day. It died out during the second world war, although there has been a modern revival.

Letter to Andrew Macphail, April 18, 1910

Rather a serous thing has happened. The cuckoo is four days late! He should have been let out of the basket by Old Woman at Heathfield cuckoo-fair on the 14th and not a sound have we heard. The wife was on the road that day and testifies that all libations etc were duly offered (for she met any amount of drunken men on the Heathfield road) so I fear that the cuckoo means to forsake England.

CUCKOO SONG

Tell it to the locked-up trees,
Cuckoo, bring your song here!
Warrant, Act and Summons, please,
For Spring to pass along here!
Tell old Winter, if he doubt,
Tell him squat and square – a!
Old Woman!
Old Woman!
Old Woman's let the Cuckoo out
At Heffle Cuckoo Fair – a!

March has searched and April tried –
'Tisn't long to May now.
Not so far to Whitsuntide
And Cuckoo's come to stay now!
Hear the valiant fellow shout
Down the orchard bare – a!
Old Woman!
Old Woman!
Old Woman's let the Cuckoo out
At Heffle Cuckoo Fair – a!

When your heart is young and gay
And the season rules it –
Work your works and play your play
'Fore the Autumn cools it!
Kiss you turn and turn-about,
But, my lad, beware – a!
Old Woman!
Old Woman!
Old Woman's let the Cuckoo out
At Heffle Cuckoo Fair – a!

The Burial of Edward VII

Kipling resisted all political honours throughout his life, fearing the taint of compromise, but his respect for the monarchy is clear in this letter to his son, who was at a boarding school in Rottingdean. His appreciation of Edward VII reminds us of the headline the 'Times' would use when Kipling and George V died within days of each other in 1936: 'The King is dead and has taken his trumpeter with him'.

Letter to John, May 20, 1910
Dear old man –
This has been one of the most wonderful days that ever I remember. In the first place it was the first day of real summer weather – hot but not too hot with a wind that drove away the thunder-clouds. In the second place it was more of a Sunday than anything you could imagine. Last night was hot and sultry with bright white lightning, winking and flashing far away towards the East: now and then one heard (I was up about 2 a.m. to listen to it) a low growl of thunder and then the rain fell in a steady warm drip, same as at Cape Town.

I was afraid it might turn to storm by daylight and so spoil all the arrangements for the funeral procession through London: but it all cleared away by morning and from eight or nine o'clock everything was as perfect as it could be. But (I wonder if this was the case at Rottingdean) the stillness all over the fields and in the air was much deeper than the ordinary stillness of a Sunday. Nobody was in the fields; no one was driving sheep or cattle so one did not hear any distant lowing or bleating; nobody was driving a horse or getting a fallow ploughed, or packing pigs into market carts. It was absolute stillness. I listened long and often but except for the bees there was nothing. You see, all England – literally all our Empire – was getting ready for the King's burial. (The South-Eastern Railway had stopped its traffic and after a while as one listened one realised that what one was waiting for was a railroad whistle.) I expect it will be a long time before one hears all England as still as a Church. I couldn't help thinking that all over the world – in Canada, Australia, India and Africa – work was stopped and held up till the King should have been buried.

We knocked off all work at Bateman's altogether. I only asked the men to attend the memorial service at one o'clock with their medals. Hobbs wore both his; Drowbridge as a Territorial had to go to Ticehurst with his Company. He was in full uniform. Martin and Moore went in black and all the maids went too. The only one left behind was Mrs Martin. As we started for Church we met the Policeman. He had come down to keep an eye on Bateman's, while it was empty. That was kind of him. We went by the fields. There was nobody in sight: one could just hear the bell tolling, muffled (I wish you would find out how they muffle a bell) through the hot still air. The street was empty; every blind was drawn; all shutters were up. There wasn't a dog in the streets.

We came half an hour before service. A few people were in their places then, and afterwards they came in – they crept in, would be the proper description – one by one till there was not a vacant seat in the Church. There was a little purple riband on one or two places as a sign of mourning but really everyone was so much in earnest that mourning did not matter. Of course you had the same service as we had so I won't tell you about that. We sang 'Peace, perfect peace'; 'O God our help in ages past'; then we had 'Crossing the Bar' as an anthem, and then Hymn 185 'The Saints of God'. I don't think much of it myself.

Colonel Feilden read the lesson. It was the one they always read when people are buried but never in all my born days did I hear it read as Colonel Feilden delivered it. I did not know it for the same thing – he spoke so beautifully, so clearly and with so much feeling. It is a splendid thing to read well! I had heard the chapter at Rottingdean when Uncle Crom was buried but this time, as the Colonel read it, it just went to my heart. He wore all his medals (except the Confederate medal for valour): the C.B; one Mutiny medal; one Boer War 1881; one Polar Expedition with the snow-white ribbon; and one 1900–02 Boer War medal. I never saw him look so handsome or so young and as I have said, his voice was wonderful and his reading was perfection. The service ended about 2.10. We all went out quietly and so home across the fields. No one spoke above a whisper in the streets as they went home. Talk of Sunday! Sunday wasn't in it for the Sundified feeling of the day. Elsie said she was quite shocked to see anyone knitting. She and Miss Goode walked together. The maids took up the whole of one pew – Georgine, Ada, Ellen, Long Nellie and Elsie Martin in a line. I don't know whether Nellie Beeching went. The Chapel people had their Memorial Service at 3 p.m. but most of them went to the Church service too. All the Sunday School children were there. As they settled down into their places one of the boys (happy boy!) managed to kick a tin under one of the benches with his feet, and instantly you saw all the boys' faces lighted with one grin of pure joy. I can't think what on earth the tin was unless it was a dustpan someone had left under a bench.

But seriously, it is a great day to have lived through. I expect it must have been impressive at your school service at Rottingdean. Out here in the quiet green country it was tremendously impressive. One saw just the ordinary everyday people, who after all make the world, just grieving for the loss of their own King and friend as they would grieve for anyone of their own blood and kin. The number of medals was astonishing. I won't afflict you with the moral of it, old man, but it's a gentle hint to us all to play the game and do our work, for the King did his and died in the doing of it just as much as if he'd been shot on active service. And he was a great King. We are too near to realise how big a man he was, but when you are my age you'll see it clearly.

All were here though Mummy a little tired, and the pups behaving scandalously. They are feeling gay and strong. They fight like fiends and Bet gets on the top of her kennel where Jack can't reach her and then he gives tongue like a Comanche Indian. I walked 'em over to Lost Meadow today and they followed me splendidly. They are good dogs and Jack has tons of character. Likewise he will make a hefty fighter. I don't think he knows fear.

Several of the Kiplings' pets are buried in the garden at Bateman's.

To Andrew Macphail, August 1910

Here's our first day of summer – after summer is dead. The blackberries are setting; wild roses over; meadowsweet half over and the hay (six weeks late!) lying about the fields and all the while we've had nowt but grey skies and chill winds. Even now the clouds look greasy and thundersome. D'you know anything about village flower shows – with tents, the village band (more quickly caught than a pestilence and the taker runs presently mad) cocoa-nut shies, dancing on the grass, prize givings for butter, home baked bread, collections of vegetable produce, table decorations, needlework etc etc. Because this is the season for 'em and next week the village will have its own flower show at Bateman's. This means that the entire population will decant itself into and over our garden and the next field; will dance on the lawn till 9.30 p.m. and will generally possess and devastate the whole place with the cheeriest goodwill in the world.

Nota. Our head gardener who bears the brunt of the fray and will have to clean up later is on the committee so his mouth is shut. The local grocer (also a church warden) and the school teacher came down

The squash court Kipling had built for his son John at Bateman's now has a corrugated iron roof and houses gardening machinery.

here yesterday to choose sites for tents and to fill the back yard with tables, trestles, marquee poles etc etc and incidentally to talk things over.

It's all as easy as an old shoe and as old as Bateman's itself in point of custom, ritual and prescription. And so it do make me laugh when the recently-escaped offspring of Slovonia thinly disguised as 'citizens' of the U.S. talk and write about 'democracy'. They aren't within Marconi-distance of it. We went to the show in the next village – Brightling – yesterday where tucked away among beech-tree woods is an old Georgian house with a hanging garden, walled, ancient and pine-fringed, that would make you weep with joy at the continuity of things. And there was the next village at ease in its own Zion – the mere fact that the house and gardens were let to strangers concerned it not one whit. The house – stone and indestructible – had always been the preordained place for flower shows on stated occasions and that custom couldn't be altered. After all (says the platitudinarian) it's the total institutions that matter – not the individual barbarian. But my lawn will be pounded to bits by their feet.

A GAME AT SQUASH

Letter to John, June 25, 1912
You will be pleased to learn that three sides of the squash court have been finished. The floor and the back wall have still to be done but I hope that won't take long. The size of the court is within a few inches exactly standard size. We are 29'8" long: standard is 30! Our back wall is 8'6" which is exactly standard and our playing wall is 16 feet – two feet higher than standard. I do hope it will be a success. It almost tempts me to go in for the game. I was at the Stores a few days ago (wish you had been with me!) and bought the rackets and balls – three rackets and half a dozen balls. I had no idea that the rackets were so heavy.

Letter to John, July 2, 1912
Meantime our squash court is up – all four walls done. Three of 'em plastered and painted black: the floor levelled and concreted, and all that remains is to put down the bricks. E[lsie] went up there the other day with one of the new rackets and a ball and swiped about. E. is a great tennis player but does not savvy squash. She ducked and fled from the little hard red ball as it returned off the wall – rather as if she were shut up in a room with a buck-hornet. I think it's going to be a spiffing court. Likewise one can play fives in it.

John was 17 when his father wrote this letter, and just 18 when he was reported wounded and missing the following September. A note at the top reads '(a vile misty wet morning) 8.30 a.m.'

Letter to John, February 27, 1915

Dear old man,

The billettees (I don't know how you spell it) have just gone to pick up their men in Burwash and to march back to Eastbourne via Dallington and Pevensey. I think they have had a good time of it. They turned up yesterday evening about 6.30 (having ordered dinner for that hour). They were preceded by a young transport officer (Preeston was his name) who rather reminded us of you. Also three or four soldier servants carried their kit to Bateman's – and you can imagine the joy of the maids.

The bell-pull by the front door at Bateman's came from The Grange, the former London home of Kipling's Burne-Jones aunt and uncle – a retreat for him as a boy during his unhappy time at 'The House of Desolation' in Southsea.

'I can remember as a small child having to jump up to catch hold of it,' he wrote, 'and it was to me in those days a sort of "open sesame" into a House Beautiful.'

When he bought Bateman's 'I begged for and was given that bell-pull for my entrance, in the hope that other children might also feel happy when they rang it.'

There were six chaps altogether – a Captain Dryden with a North-country accent that you could cut with a brick; a Glasgow boy with a ditto Scotch accent; another Scotchman and the rest mixed and curious but all interesting – Dryden, Cooper, Brown, Goodman, Nicholson, Andrews was the full list. They had posted sentries and outposts over by Sutherland Harris's and had set the rest of their company to digging trenches near the golf course. Apparently the 10th Battn Loyal North Lancs love trench-digging.

We gave them a decent dinner – tomato soup, fish, mutton, mince pies and cheese straws, and unlimited ginger beer and cigarettes. They, naturally, talked shop all the time. Three of 'em had been in the Public School battalions and had got their commissions from the ranks. They said it was a great pull in the New Armies, if a man had passed through this mill. They said that the weakness of the new armies was in the NCOs, and they told me awful yarns of Sergeants (aged 21) larking with the men. Of the men themselves they could not speak too highly. One of the officers was at Tidworth with the 6th N.N. Lancs – Henry Longbottom's battn before he joined the R.F.C. He said that that battn was a set of first class sweeps and rapparees but that they came to heel in a very short time. Four of the officers got out at ten to inspect trenches, outposts etc. They were hung with revolver, binoculars, water bottle and all whole mass of muckings . . .

Well, at eleven, the four officers on duty returned. They were very pleased with the trenches etc etc. We gave them drinks and sandwiches and they went to bed: one in the dimity room; two in the big guest room; two in the north room upstairs; and one in the room that used to be my father's. They were as quiet as mice. We gave 'em breakfast at 7.45 and handed 'em their lunches to eat on the road and we parted with expressions of the highest esteem on both sides. It was a pretty wet day and I feel sorry for 'em. But there's no doubt that the new armies work like beavers and they are getting some sort of discipline. You seem to have come in for a lot of heavy work – digging trenches in snow storms is no catch. I wish you'd send us a line telling us when you are likely to be in town. It's more than a week since we met – or will be when this letter reaches you – and after the month at Brown's I feel that a week is a very long time.

Now I'll shut up and send this letter in the post.

With all our best love, Ever affectionately,
Your father

P.S. I've got my new fountain pen (a Waterman's) in perfect working order and don't intend to use any other till I've broken it.

'Have you news of my boy Jack?'
    Not this tide.
'When d'you think that he'll come back?'
    Not with this wind blowing, and this tide.

'Has any one else had word of him?'
    Not this tide.
For what is sunk will hardly swim,
    Not with this wind blowing, and this tide.

'Oh, dear, what comfort can I find'
    None this tide,
    Nor any tide,
Except he did not shame his kind –
    Not even with that wind blowing, and that tide.

Then hold your head up all the more,
    This tide,
    And every tide;
Because he was the son you bore,
And gave to that wind blowing and that tide!

Oak, Ash and Thorn

The Puck stories collected in the two books *Puck of Pook's Hill* and *Rewards and Fairies* (published in 1906 and 1910 respectively) are steeped in Sussex lore, much of it set in the Burwash area with Bateman's as its epicentre. Kipling explained his purpose in a letter to Edward Bok: 'They're part of a scheme of mine for trying to give children not a notion of history but a notion of the time sense which is at the bottom of all knowledge of history, and history rightly understanded means love of one's fellow men and the lands one lives in.'

During the same period he was collaborating with C.L.R. Fletcher, an historian he admired, on *A School History of England*, published in 1911. (He wrote poems to accompany Fletcher's text.) Something of its flavour is conveyed by the authors' declaration that their work was intended 'for all boys and girls who are interested in the story of Great Britain and her Empire'.

Children and their reading habits have changed since Kipling's day. *The Jungle Book* and the *Just So Stories* are more often discovered at the cinema or in front of the television screen than on the printed page, and the Puck tales have the additional handicap for today's sophisticated youngsters of having a fairy as their main character. In addition, the 'child leads' (Una and Dan, loosely representing Elsie and John) have little more than walk-on parts: their role is simply to be introduced to the English pageant by Puck, whose 'oak, ash and thorn' magic conjures up a wide range of characters from pre-history through the Romans, Saxons and Normans to Elizabethan England and the heyday of the smugglers along the Sussex coast.

Kipling suggested that the stories were written as much for adults as for children, but tastes have changed here too, and it's difficult to believe that they will enjoy much of a revival. For Sussex readers who know something of the background, however, they offer pleasing slants on familiar characters and events. We meet Sir Richard Dalyngridge, who came over with the Conqueror and was granted the manor that embraced the land where Bateman's now stands. We learn what happened when the first

Queen Elizabeth passed through Northiam ('Norgem' to the locals) on her way to inspect the Fleet at Rye – her little green shoes can still be seen today in the house called Brickwall. St Wilfrid, who converted Sussex to Christianity, recalls a miracle involving a seal from Manhood End, while the herbalist and astrologer Nicholas Culpeper tells the children about an outbreak of the plague in Burwash and reveals that the drinking-trough used by their hens was the original plague-stone set up on the village boundary.

Kipling can sometimes prove difficult to fathom because he makes few concessions to readers unfamiliar with his widespread references – to the Bible and the Classics, for instance; to social and religious nuances in his Indian stories; to the arcana of the men's worlds he liked to infiltrate for his poems and short stories. By his own admission, when writing *Rewards and Fairies* he 'loaded the book up with allegories and allusions' and then laboured mightily to disguise his efforts, 'trying not to let the joins show'. This is Kipling the craftsman, revelling in his skills, yet keeping them hidden. As he says elsewhere, 'I specially don't want people to notice my "style"'.

Pook's Hill rises behind Bateman's.

Puck of Pook's Hill

The ten stories collected as 'Puck of Pook's Hill' were first published in 'Strand' magazine from January to October 1906, with illustrations by Claude Shepperson. As with much of Kipling's fiction, the narrative was accompanied by complementary verses.

Puck's Song

See you the ferny ride that steals
Into the oak-woods far?
O that was whence they hewed the keels
That rolled to Trafalgar.

And mark you where the ivy clings
To Bayham's mouldering walls?
O there we cast the stout railings
That stand around St Paul's.

See you the dimpled track that runs
All hollow through the wheat?
O that was where they hauled the guns
That smote King Philip's fleet.

(Out of the Weald, the secret Weald),
Men sent in ancient years
The horse-shoes red at Flodden Field,
The arrows at Poitiers!)

See you our little mill that clacks,
So busy by the brook?
She has ground her corn and paid her tax
Ever since Domesday Book.

See you our stilly woods of oak,
And the dreadful ditch beside?
O that was where the Saxons broke
On the day that Harold died.

Above left: 'Bayham's mouldering walls'; right: ancient Rye.

See you the windy levels spread
About the gates of Rye?
O that was where the Northmen fled,
When Alfred's ships came by.

See you our pastures wide and lone,
Where the red oxen browse?
O there was a City thronged and known,
Ere London boasted a house.

And see you, after rain, the trace
Of mound and ditch and wall?
O that was a Legion's camping-place,
When Caesar sailed from Gaul.

And see you the marks that show and fade,
Like shadows on the Downs?
O they are the lines the Flint Men made,
To guard their wondrous towns.

Trackway and Camp and City lost,
Salt Marsh where now is corn –
Old Wars, old Peace, old Arts that cease,
And so was England born!

She is not any common Earth,
Water or wood or air,
But Merlin's Isle of Gramarye,
Where you and I will fare!

In cleaning out an old pond which might have been an ancient marl-pit or mine-head, we dredged two intact Elizabethan 'sealed quarts' that Christopher Sly affected, all pearly with the patina of centuries. Its deepest mud yielded us a perfectly polished Neolithic axe-head with but one chip on its still venomous edge.

These things are detailed that you may understand how, when my cousin, Ambrose Poynter, said to me: 'Write a yarn about Roman times here,' I was interested. 'Write,' said he, 'about an old Centurion of the Occupation telling his experiences to his children.' 'What is his name?' I demanded, for I move easiest from a given point. 'Parnesius,' said my cousin; and the name stuck in my head. I was then on Committee of Ways and Means (which had grown to include Public Works and Communications) but, in due season, the name came back – with seven other inchoate devils. I went off Committee, and began to 'hatch', in which state I was 'a brother to dragons and a companion to owls'.

Just beyond the west fringe of our land, in a little valley running from Nowhere to Nothing-at-all, stood the long, overgrown slag-heap of a most ancient forge, supposed to have been worked by the Phoenicians and Romans and, since then, uninterruptedly till the middle of the eighteenth century. The bracken and rush-patches still hid stray pigs of iron, and if one scratched a few inches through the rabbit-shaven turf, one came on the narrow mule-tracks of peacock-hued furnace-slag laid down in Elizabeth's day. The ghost of a road climbed up out of this dead arena, and crossed our fields, where it was known as The Gunway, and popularly connected with Armada times. Every foot of that little corner was alive with ghosts and shadows.

Then, it pleased our children to act for us, in the open, what they remembered of *A Midsummer-Night's Dream*. Then a friend gave them a real birch-bark canoe, drawing at least three inches, in which they went adventuring on the brook. And in a near pasture of the water-meadows lay out an old and unshifting Fairy Ring.

You see how patiently the cards were stacked and dealt into my hands? The Old Things of our Valley glided into every aspect of our outdoor works. Earth, Air, Water and People had been – I saw it at last – in full conspiracy to give me ten times as much as I could compass, even if I wrote a complete history of England, as that might have touched or reached our Valley.

I went off at score – not on Parnesius, but a story told in a fog by a petty Baltic pirate, who had brought his galley to Pevensey and, off Beachy Head – where in the War we heard merchant ships being torpedoed – had passed the Roman fleet abandoning Britain to her doom. That tale may have served as a pipe-opener, but one could not see its wood for its trees, so I threw it away.

I carried the situation to the little house in Wiltshire, where my Father and Mother were installed; and smoked it over with the Father, who said – not for the first time: 'Most things in this world are accomplished by judicious leaving alone.' So we played cribbage (he had carved a perfect Lama and a little Kim for my two pegs), while the Mother worked beside us, or, each taking a book, lapsed into the silence of entire mutual comprehension. One night, apropos of nothing at all, the Father said: 'And you'll have to look up your references rather more carefully, won't you?' That had *not* been my distinction on the little *Civil and Military*.

This led me on another false scent. I wrote a tale told by Daniel Defoe in a brickyard (we had a real one of our own at that time where we burned bricks for barns and cottages to the exact tints we desired) of how he had been sent to stampede King James II, then havering about Thames mouth, out of an England where no party had any use for him. It turned out a painstaken and meritorious piece of work, overloaded with verified references, with about as much feeling to it as a walking-stick. So it also was discarded, with a tale of Doctor Johnson telling the children how he had once thrown his spurs out of a boat in Scotland, to the amazement of one Boswell.

Evidently my Daemon would not function in brickyards or school-rooms. Therefore, like Alice in Wonderland, I turned my back on the whole thing and walked the other way. Therefore, the whole thing set and linked itself. I fell first upon Normans and Saxons. Parnesius came later, directly out of a little wood above the Phoenician forge; and the rest of the tales in *Puck of Pook's Hill* followed in order. The Father came over to see us and, hearing 'Hal o' the Draft', closed in with fore-reaching pen, presently ousted me from my table, and inlaid the description of Hal's own drawing-knife. He liked that tale, and its companion piece 'The Wrong Thing' [*Rewards and Fairies*], which latter he embellished, notably in respect to an Italian fresco-worker, whose work never went 'deeper than the plaster'. He said that 'judicious leaving alone' did not apply between artists.

Of 'Dymchurch Flit', with which I was always unashamedly content, he asked: 'Where did you get that lighting from?' It had come of itself. *Qua* workmanship, that tale and two night-pieces in 'Cold Iron' [*Rewards and Fairies*] are the best in that kind I have ever made, but somehow 'The Treasure and the Law' [*Puck of Pook's Hill*] always struck me as too heavy for its frame.

Yet that tale brought me a prized petty triumph. I had put a well into the wall of Pevensey Castle *circa* AD 1100, because I needed it there.

Archaeologically, it did not exist till this year (1935) when excavators brought such a well to light. But that I maintain was a reasonable gamble. Self-contained castles must have self-contained water supplies.

Medusa mosaic at Bignor Roman Villa.

A longer chance that I took in my Roman tales was when I quartered the Seventh Cohort of the Thirtieth (Ulpia Victrix) Legion on the Wall, and asserted that there Roman troops used arrows against the Picts. The first shot was based on honest 'research'; the second was legitimate inference. Years after the tale was told, a digging-party on the Wall sent me some heavy four-sided, Roman-made, 'killing' arrows found *in situ* and – most marvellously – a rubbing of a memorial-tablet to the Seventh Cohort of the Thirtieth Legion! Having been brought up in a suspicious school, I suspected a 'leg-pull' here, but was assured that the rubbing was perfectly genuine.

A THREE-PART SONG

I'm just in love with all these three,
The Weald and the Marsh and the Down countree.
Nor I don't know which I love the most,
The Weald or the Marsh or the white Chalk coast!

I've buried my heart in a ferny hill,
Twix' a liddle low shaw an' a great high gill.
Oh, hop-bine yaller an' wood-smoke blue,
I reckon you'll keep her middling true!

I've loosed my mind for to out and run
On a Marsh that was old when Kings begun.
Oh, Romney Level and Brenzett reeds,
I reckon you know what my mind needs!

I've given my soul to the Southdown grass,
And sheep-bells tinkled where you pass.
Oh, Firle an' Ditchling an' sails at sea,
I reckon you keep my soul for me!

This is the first of the Puck stories. Elsie later explained its provenance: 'One summer in the early 1900s we children and my father acted scenes from "A Midsummer Night's Dream". Our stage was an old grass-grown quarry and there my brother as Puck, myself as Titania and my father as Bottom rehearsed and acted happily. A most realistic cardboard donkey's head had been donned by Bottom for his part, and the village policeman, passing along the lane, was amazed to see the familiar tweed-clad figure of my father topped by this extraordinary headgear.'

The children were at the Theatre, acting to Three Cows as much as they could remember of *Midsummer Night's Dream*. Their father had made them a small play out of the big Shakespeare one, and they had rehearsed it with him and with their mother till they could say it by heart. They began when Nick Bottom the weaver comes out of the bushes with a donkey's head on his shoulders, and finds Titania, Queen of the Fairies, asleep. Then they skipped to the part where Bottom asks three little fairies to scratch his head and bring him honey, and they ended where he falls asleep in Titania's arms. Dan was Puck and Nick Bottom, as well as all three Fairies. He wore a pointy-eared cloth cap for Puck, and a paper donkey's head out of Christmas cracker – but it tore if you were not careful – for Bottom. Una was Titania, with a wreath of columbines and a foxglove wand.

The Theatre lay in a meadow called the Long Slip. A little mill-stream, carrying water to a mill two or three fields away, bent round one corner of it, and in the middle of the bend lay a large old Fairy Ring of darkened grass, which was the stage. The mill-stream banks, overgrown with willow, hazel and guelder-rose, made convenient places to wait in till your turn came; and a grown-up who had seen it said that Shakespeare himself could not have imagined a more suitable setting for his play. They were not, of course, allowed to act on Midsummer Night itself, but they went down after tea on Midsummer Eve, when the shadows were growing, and they took their supper – hard-boiled eggs, Bath Oliver biscuits and salt in an envelope – with them. Three Cows had been milked and were grazing steadily with a tearing noise that one could hear all down the meadow; and the noise of the Mill at work sounded like bare feet running on hard ground. A cuckoo sat on a gate-post singing his broken June tune, 'cuckoo-cuck', while a busy kingfisher crossed from the mill-stream, to the brook which ran on the other side of the meadow. Everything else was a sort of thick, sleepy stillness smelling of meadow-sweet and dry grass.

Their play went beautifully. Dan remembered all his parts – Puck, Bottom and the three Fairies – and Una never forgot a word of Titania – not even the difficult piece where she tells the Fairies how to feed Bottom with 'apricocks, green figs and dewberries', and all the lines end in 'ies'. They were both so spleased that they acted it three times over from beginning to end before they sat down in the unthistly centre of the Ring to eat eggs and Bath Olivers. This was when they heard a whistle among the alders on the bank, and they jumped.

The bushes parted. In the very spot where Dan had stood as Puck they saw a small, brown, broad-shouldered, pointy-eared person with a snub nose, slanting blue eyes and a grin that ran right across his freckled face. He shaded his forehead as though he were watching Quince, Snout, Bottom and the others rehearsing *Pyramus and Thisbe*, and, in a voice as deep as Three Cows asking to be milked, he began:

> *What hempen homespuns have we swaggering here,*
> *So near the cradle of the fairy Queen?*

He stopped, hollowed one hand round his ear, and, with a wicked twinkle in his eye, went on:

> *What, a play toward? I'll be an auditor;*
> *An actor, too, perhaps, if I see cause.*

The children looked and gasped. The small thing – he was no taller than Dan's shoulder – stepped quietly into the Ring.

'I'm rather out of practice,' said he; 'but that's the way my part ought to be played.'

Still the children stared at him – from his dark-blue cap, like a big columbine flower, to his bare, hairy feet. At last he laughed.

'Please don't look like that. It isn't *my* fault. What else could you expect?' he said.

'We didn't expect anyone,' Dan answered slowly. 'This is our field.'

'Is it?' said their visitor, sitting down. 'Then what on Human Earth made you act *Midsummer Night's Dream* three times over, *on* Midsummer Eve, *in* the middle of a Ring, and under – right *under* one of my oldest hills in Old England? Pook's Hill – Puck's Hill – Puck's Hill – Pook's Hill! It's as plain as the nose on my face.'

He pointed to the bare, fern-coloured slope of Pook's Hill that runs up from the far side of the mill-stream to a dark wood. Beyond that wood the ground rises and rises for five hundred feet, till at last you climb out on the bare top of Beacon Hill, to look over the Pevensey Levels and the Channel and half the naked South Downs.

'By Oak, Ash and Thorn!' he cried, still laughing. 'If this had happened a few hundred years ago you'd have had all the People of the Hills out like bees in June!'

'We didn't know it was wrong,' said Dan.

'Wrong!' The little fellow shook with laughter. 'Indeed, it isn't wrong. You've done something that Kings and Knights and Scholars in old days would have given their crowns and spurs and books to find out. If Merlin himself had helped you, you couldn't have managed better! You've broken the Hills – you've broken the Hills! It hasn't happened in a thousand years.'

'We – we didn't mean to,' said Una.

'Of course you didn't!' That just why you did it. Unluckily the Hills are empty now, and all the People of the Hills are gone. I'm the only one left. I'm Puck, the oldest Old Thing in England, very much at your service if – if you care to have anything to do with me. If you don't, of course you've only to say so, and I'll go.'

He looked at the children, and the children looked at him for quite half a minute. His eyes did not twinkle any more. They were very kind, and there was the beginning of a good smile on his lips.

Una put out her hand.

'Don't go,' she said. 'We like you.'

'Have a Bath Oliver,' said Dan, and he passed over the squashy envelope with the eggs.

'By Oak, Ash and Thorn,' cried Puck, taking off his blue cap. 'I like you too. Sprinkle a plenty salt on the biscuit, Dan, and I'll eat it with you. That'll show you the sort of person I am. Some of us' – he went on, with his mouth full – 'couldn't abide Salt, or Horse-shoes over a door, or Mountain-ash berries, or Running Water, or Cold Iron, or the sound of Church Bells. But I'm Puck!'

He brushed the crumbs crefully from his doublet and shook hands.

'We always said, Dan and I,' Una stammered, 'that if it ever happened we'd know ex-actly what to do; but – but now it seems all different somehow.'

'She means meeting a fairy,' said Dan. 'I never believed in 'em – not after I was six, anyhow.'

'I did,' said Una. 'At least, I sort of half believed till we learned "Farewell, Rewards". Do you know "Farewell, Rewards and Fairies"?'

'Do you mean this?' said Puck. He threw his big head back and began at the second line:

> *Good housewives now may say,*
> *For now foul sluts in dairies*
> *Do fare as well as they;*
> *And though they weep their hearths no less*

('Join in, Una!')

> *Than maids were wont to do,*
> *Yet who of late for cleanliness*
> *Finds sixpence in her shoe?'*

The echoes flapped along the flat meadow.

'Of course I know it,' he said.

'And then there's the verse about the Rings,' said Dan. 'When I was little it always meade me feel unhappy in my inside.'

' "Witness those rings and roundelays", do you mean?' boomed Puck, with a voice like a great church organ.

> *Of theirs which yet remain,*
> *Were footed in Queen Mary's days*
> *On many a grassy plain,*
> *But since of late Elizabeth,*
> *And, later, James came in,*
> *Are never seen on any heath*
> *As when the time hath been.*

'It's some time since I heard that sung, but there's no good beating about the bush: it's true. The People of the Hills have left. I saw them come into Old England and I saw them go. Giants, trolls, kelpies, brownies, goblins, imps; wood, tree, mount and water spirits; heath-people, hill-watchers, treasure-guards, good people, little people, pishogues, leprechauns, night-riders, pixies, nixies, gnomes and the rest – gone, all gone!

'I came into England with Oak, Ash and Thorn, and when Oak, Ash and Thorn are gone I shall go too.'

Dan looked round the meadow – at Una's Oak by the lower gate; at the line of ash trees that overhang Otter Pool where the mill-stream spills over when the Mill does not need it, and at the gnarled old white-thorn where Three Cows scratched their necks.

'It's all right,' he said, and added, 'I'm planting a lot of acorns this autumn, too.'

'Then aren't you most awfully old?' said Una.

'Not old – fairly long-lived, as folks say hereabouts. Let me see – my friends used to set my dish of cream for me o'nights when Stonehenge was new. Yes, before the Flint Men made the Dewpond under Chanctonbury Ring.'

Una clasped her hands, cried 'Oh!' and nodded her head.

'She's thought a plan,' Dan explained. 'She always does like that when she thinks a plan.'

'I was thinking – suppose we saved some of our porridge and put it in the attic for you? They'd notice if we left it in the nursery.'

'Schoolroom,' said Dan quickly, and Una flushed, because they had made a solemn treaty that summer not to call the schoolroom the nursery any more.

'Bless your heart o' gold,' said Puck. 'You'll make a fine considering wench some market-day. I really don't want you to put out a bowl for me; but if ever I need a bite, be sure I'll tell you.'

He stretched himself at length on the dry grass, and the children stretched out beside him, their bare legs waving happily in the air. They felt they could not be afraid of him any more than of their particular friend old Hobden the hedger. He did not bother them with grown-up questions, or laugh at the donkey's head, but lay and smiled to himself in the most sensible way.

'Have you a knife on you?' he said at last.

Dan handed over his big one-bladed outdoor knife, and Puck began to carve out a piece of turf from the centre of the Ring.

'What's that for – Magic?' said Una, as he pressed up the square of chocolate loam that cut like so much cheese.

'One of my little magics,' he answered, and cut another. 'You see, I can't let you into the Hills because the People of the Hills have gone; but if you care to take seisin from me, I may be able to show you something out of the common here on Human Earth. You certainly deserve it.'

'What's taking seisin?' said Dan, cautiously.

'It's an old custom the people had when they bought and sold land. They used to cut out a clod and hand it over to the buyer, and you weren't lawfully seised of your land – it didn't really belong to you – till the other fellow had actually given you a piece of it – like this.' He held out the turves.

'But it's our own meadow,' said Dan, drawing back. 'Are you going to magic it away?'

Puck laughed. 'I know it's your meadow, but there's a great deal more in it than you or your father ever guessed. Try!'

He turned his eyes on Una.

'I'll do it,' she said. Dan followed her example at once.

'Now are you two lawfully seised and possessed of all Old England,' began Puck, in a sing-song voice. 'By right of Oak, Ash and Thorn are you free to come and go and look and know where I shall show or best you please. You shall see What you shall see and you shall hear What you shall hear, though It shall have happened three thousand year; and you shall know neither Doubt nor Fear. Fast! Hold fast all I give you.'

The children shut their eyes, but nothing happened.

'Well?' said Una, disappointedly opening them. 'I thoght there would be dragons.'

' "Though it shall have happened three thousand year," ' said Puck, and counted on his fingers. 'No; I'm afraid there were no dragons three thousand years ago.'

'But there hasn't happened anything at all,' said Dan.

'Wait awhile,' said Puck. 'You don't grow an oak in a year – and Old England's older than twenty oaks. Let's sit down again and think. I can do that for a century at a time.'

'Ah, but you're a fairy,' said Dan.

'Have you ever heard me say that word yet?' said Puck quickly.

'No. You talk about "the People of the Hills", but you never say "fairies",' said Una. 'I was wondering at that. Don't you like it?'

'How would you like to be called "mortal' or "human being" all the time?' said Puck; 'or "son of Adam" or "daughter of Eve"?'

'I shouldn't like it at all,' said Dan. 'That's how the Djinns and Afrits talk in the *Arabian Nights.*'

'And that's how *I* feel about saying – that word that I don't say. Besides, what you call *them* are made-up things the People of the Hills have never heard of – little buzzflies with butterfly wings and gauze petticoats, and shiny stars in their hair, and a wand like a schoolteacher's cane for punishing bad boys and rewarding good ones. *I* know 'em!'

'We don't mean that sort,' said Dan. 'We hate 'em, too.'

'Exactly,' said Puck. 'Can you wonder that the People of the Hills don't care to be confused with that painty-winged, wand-waving, sugar-and-shake-your-head set of impostors? Butterfly wings, indeed! I've seen Sir Huon and a troop of his people setting off from Tintagel Castle for Hy-Brasil in the teeth of a sou'-westerly gale, with the spray flying all over the Castle, and the Horses of the Hills wild with fright. Out they'd go in a lull, screaming like gulls, and back they'd be driven five good miles inland before they could come head to wind again. Butterfly-wings! It was Magic – Magic as black as Merlin could make it, and the whole sea was green fire and white foam with singing mermaids in it. And the Horses of the Hills picked their way from one wave to another by the lightning flashes! *That* was how it was in the old days!'

'Splendid,' said Dan, but Una shuddered.

'I'm glad they're gone, then; but what made the People of the Hills go away?' Una asked.

'Different things. I'll tell you one of them some day – the thing that made the biggest flit of any,' said Puck. 'But they didn't all flit at once. They dropped off, one by one, through the centuries. Most of them were foreigners who couldn't stand our climate. *They* flitted early.

'How early?' said Dan.

'A couple of thousand years or more. The fact is they began as Gods. The Phoenicians brought some over when they came to buy tin; and the Gauls, and the Jutes, and the Danes, and the Frisians, and the Angles brought more when they landed. They were always landing in those days, or being driven back to their ships, and they always brought their Gods with them. England is a bad country for Gods. Now, *I* began as I mean to go on. A bowl of porridge, a dish of milk and a little quiet fun with the country folk in the lanes was enough for me then, as it is now. I belong here, you see, and I have been mixed up with people all my days. But most of the others insisted on being Gods, and having temples, and altars, and priests and sacrifices of their own.'

'People burned in wicker baskets?' said Dan. 'Like Miss Blake tells us about?'

'All sorts of sacrifices,' said Puck. 'If it wasn't men, it was horses, or cattle, or pigs or metheglin – that's a sticky, sweet sort of beer. *I* never like it. They were a stiff-necked, extravagant set of idols, the Old Things. But what was the result? Men don't like being sacrificed at the best of times; they don't even like sacrificing their farm-horses. After a while men simply left the Old Things alone, and the roofs of their temples fell in, and the Old Things had to scuttle out and pick up a living as they could. Some of them took to hanging about trees, and hiding in graves and groaning o' nights. If they groaned loud enough and long enough they might frighten a poor countryman into sacrificing a hen, or leaving a pound of butter for them. I remember one Goddess called Belisama. She became a common wet water-spirit somewhere in Lancashire. And there were hundreds of other friends of mine. First they were Gods. Then they were People of the Hills, and then they flitted to other places because they couldn't get on with the English for one reason or another. There was only one Old Thing, I remember, who honestly worked for his living after he came down in the world. He was called Weland, and he was a smith to some Gods. I've forgotten their names, but he used to make them swords and spears. I think he claimed kin with Thor of the Scandinavians.'

'*Heroes of Asgard* Thor?' said Una. She had been reading the book.

'Perhaps,' answered Puck. 'None the less, when bad times came he didn't beg or steal. He worked; and I was lucky enough to be able to do him a good turn.'

'Tell us about it,' said Dan. 'I think I like hearing of Old Things.'

They rearranged themselves comfortably, each chewing a grass stem. Puck propped himself on one strong arm and went on:

'Let's think! I met Weland first on a November afternoon in a sleet storm, on Pevensey Level – '

'Pevensey? Over the hill, you mean?' Dan pointed south.

'Yes; but it was all marsh in those days, right up to Horsebridge and Hydeneye. I was on Beacon Hill – they called it Brunanburgh then – when I saw the pale flame that burning thatch makes, and I went down to look. Some pirates – I think they must have been Peofn's men – were burning a village on the Levels, and Weland's image – a big, black wooden thing with amber beads round his neck – lay in the bows of a black thirty-two-oar galley that they had just beached. Bitter cold it was! There were icicles hanging from her deck and the oars were glazed over with ice, and there was ice on Weland's lips. When he saw me he began a long chant in his own tongue, telling me how he was going to rule England, and how I should smell the smoke of his altars from Lincolnshire to the Isle of Wight. *I* didn't care! I'd seen too many Gods charging into Old England to be upset about it. I let him sing himself out while his men were burning the village, and then I said (I don't know what put it into my head), "Smith of the Gods," I said, "the time comes when I shall meet you plying your trade for hire by the wayside." '

'What did Weland say?' said Una. 'Was he angry?'

'He called me names and rolled his eyes, and I went away to wake up the people inland. But the pirates conquered the country, and for centuries Weland was a most important God. He had temples everywhere – from Lincolnshire to the Isle of Wight, as he said – and his sacrifices were simply scandalous. To do him justice, he preferred horses to men; but men *or* horses, I knew that presently he'd have to come down in the world – like the other Old Things. I gave him lots of time – I gave him about a thousand years – and at the end of 'em I went into one of his temples near Andover to see how he prospered. There was his altar, and there was his image, and there were his priests, and there were the congregation, and everybody seemed quite happy, except Weland and the priests. In the old days the congregation were unhappy until the priests had chosen their sacrifices; and so would *you* have been. When the service began a priest rushed out, dragged a man up to the altar, pretended to hit him on the head with a little gilt axe, and the man fell down and pretended to die. Then everybody shouted: "A sacrifice to Weland! A sacrifice to Weland!" '

'And the man wasn't really dead?' said Una.

'Not a bit. All as much pretence as a dolls' tea-party. Then they brought out a splendid white horse, and the priest cut some hair from its mane and tail and burned it on the altar, shouting, "A sacrifice!" That counted the same as if a man and a horse had been killed. I saw poor Weland's face through the smoke, and I couldn't help laughing. He looked so disgusted and so hungry, and all he had to satisfy himself was a horrid smell of burning hair. Just a dolls' tea-party!

'I judged it better not to say anything then ('twouldn't have been fair), and the next time I came to Andover, a few hundred years later, Weland and his temple were gone, and there was a Christian bishop in a church there. None of the People of the Hills could tell me anything about him, and I supposed that he had left England.' Puck turned, lay on his other elbow, and thought for a long time.

'Let's see,' he said at last. 'It must have been some few years later – a year or two before the Conquest, I think – that I came backt to Pook's Hill here, and one evening I heard old Hobden talking about Weland's Ford.'

'If you mean old Hobden the hedger, he's only seventy-two. He told me so himself,' said Dan. 'He's an intimate friend of ours.'

'You're quite right,' Puck replied. 'I meant old Hobden's ninth great-grandfather. He was a free man and burned charcoal hereabouts. I've known the family, father and son, so long that I get confused sometimes. Hob of the Dene was my Hobden's name, and he lived at the Forge cottage.

'Of course, I pricked up my ears when I heard Weland mentioned, and I scuttled through the woods to the ford just beyond Bog Wood yonder.' He jerked his head westward, where the valley narrows between wooded hills and steep hop-fields.

'Why, that's Willigford Bridge,' said Una. 'We go there for walks often. There's a kingfisher there.'

'It was Weland's Forge then, dearie. A road led down to it from the Beacon on the top of the hill – a shocking bad road it was – and all the hillside was thick, thick oak-forest, with deer in it. There was no trace of Weland, but presently I saw a fat old farmer riding down from the Beacon under the greenwood tree. His horse had cast a shoe in the clay, and when he came to the ford he dismounted, took a penny out of his purse, laid it on stone, tied the old horse to an oak and called out: "Smith, Smith, here is work for you!" Then he sat down and went to sleep. You can imagine how *I* felt when I saw a white-bearded, bent old blacksmith in a leather apron creep out from behind the oak and begin to shoe the horse. It was Weland himself. I was so astonished that I jumped out and said: "What on Human Earth are you doing here, Weland?" '

'Poor Weland!' sighed Una.

'He pushed the long hair back from his forehead (he didn't recognise me at first). Then he said: '*You* ought to know. You foretold it, Old Thing. I'm shoeing horses for hire. I'm not even Weland now," he said. "They call me Wayland-Smith." '

'Poor chap!' said Dan. 'What did you say?'

'What could I say? He looked up, with the horse's foot on his lap, and he said, smiling, "I remember the time when I wouldn't have accepted this old bag of bones as a sacrifice, and now I'm glad enough to shoe him for a penny."

' "Isn't there any way for you to get back to Valhalla, or wherever you come from?' I said.

' "I'm afraid not," he said, rasping away at the hoof. He had a wonderful touch with horses. The old beast was whinnying on his shoulder. "You may remember that I was not a gentle God in my Day and my Time and my Power. I shall never be released till some human being truly wishes me well."

' "Surely," said I, "the farmer can't do less than that. You're shoeing the horse all round for him."

' "Yes," said he, "and my nails will hold a shoe from one full moon to the next. But farmers and Weald clay," said he, "are both uncommon cold and sour."

'Would you believe it, that when the farmer woke and found his horse shod he rode away without one word of thanks? I was so angry that I wheeled his horse right round and walked him back three miles to the Beacon, just to teach the old sinner politeness.'

'Where you invisible?' said Una. Puck nodded, gravely.

'The Beacon was always laid in those days ready to light, in case the French landed at Pevensey; and I walked the horse about and about it that lee-long summer night. The farmer thought he was bewitched – well, he *was*, of course – and began to pray and shout. *I* didn't care! I was as good a Christian as he any fair-day in the County, and about four o'clock in the morning a young novice came along from the monastery that used to stand on the top of Beacon Hill.'

'What's a novice?' said Dan.

'It really means a man who is beginning to be a monk, but in those days people sent their sons to a monastery just the same as a school. This young fellow had been to a monastery in France for a few months every year, and he was finishing his studies in the monastery close to his home here. Hugh was his name, and he had got up to go fishing hereabouts. His people owned all lthis valley. Hugh heard the farmer shouting, and asked him what in the world he meant. The old man spun him a wonderful tale about fairies and goblins and witches; and I *know* he hadn't seen a thing except rabbits and red deer all that night. (The People of the Hills are like otters – they don't show except when they choose.) But the novice wasn't a fool. He looked down at the horse's feet and saw the new shoes fastened as only Weland knew how to fasten 'em. (Weland had a way of turning down the nails that folks called the Smith's Clinch.)

'"H'm!" said the novice. "Where did you get your horse shod?"

'The farmer wouldn't tell him at first, because the priests never liked their people to have any dealings with the Old Things. At last he confessed that the Smith had done it. "What did you pay him?" said the novice. "Penny," said the farmer, very sulkily. "That's less than a Christian would have charged," said the novice. "I hope you threw a 'thank you' into the bargain." "No," said the father; "Wayland-Smith's a heathen." "Heathen or no heathen," said the novice, "you took his help, and where you get help there you must give thanks." "What?" said the farmer – he was in a furious temper because I was walking the old horse in circles all this time – "What, you young jackanapes?" said he. "Then by your reasoning I ought to say 'Thank you' to Satan if he helped me?" "Don't roll about there splitting reasons with me," said the novice. "Come back to the Ford and thank the Smith, or you'll be sorry."

'Back the farmer had to go. I led the horse, though no one saw me, and the novice walked beside us, his gown swishing through the shiny dew and his fishing-rod across his shoulders, spear-wise. When we reached the Ford again – it was five o'clock and misty still under the oaks – the farmer simply wouldn't say "Thank you". He said he'd tell the Abbot that the novice wanted him to worship heathen Gods. Then Hugh the novice lost his temper. He just cried, "Out!" put his arm under the farmer's fat leg and heaved him from his saddle on to the turf, and before he could rise he caught him by the back of the neck and shook him like a rat till the farmer growled, "Thank you, Wayland-Smith." '

'Did Weland see all this?' said Dan.

'Oh yes, and he shouted his old war-cry when the farmer thudded on to the ground. He was delighted. Then the novice turned to the oak tree and said, "Ho, Smith of the Gods! I am ashamed of this rude farmer; but for all you have done in kindness and charity to him to others of our people, I thank you and wish you well." Then he picked up his fishing-rod – it looked more like a tall spear than ever – and tramped off down your valley.'

'And what did poor Weland do?' said Una.

'He laughed and he cried with joy, because he had been released at last, and could go away. But he was an honest Old Thing. He had worked for his living and he paid his debts before he left. "I shall give that novice a gift," said Weland. "A gift that shall do him good the wide world over and Old England after him. Blow up my fire, Old Thing, while I get the iron for my last task." Then he made a sword – a dark-grey, wavy-lined sword – and I blew the fire while he hammered. By Oak, Ash and Thorn, I tell you, Weland was a Smith of the Gods! He cooled that sword in running water twice, and the third time he cooled it in the evening dew, and he laid it out in the moonlight and said Runes (that's charms) over it, and he carved Runes of Prophecy on the blade. "Old Thing," he said to me, wiping his forehead, "this is the best blade that Weland ever made. Even the user will never know how good it is. Come to the monastery."

'We went to the dormitory where the monks slept, we saw the novice fast asleep in his cot, and Weland put the sword into his hand, and I remember the young fellow gripped it in his sleep. Then Weland strode as far as he dared into the Chapel and threw down all his shoeing-tools – his hammers and pincers and rasps – to show that he had done with them for ever. It sounded like suits of armour falling, and the sleepy monks ran in, for they thought the monastery had been attacked by the French. The novice came first of all, waving his new sword and shouting Saxon battle-cries. When they saw the shoeing-tools they were very bewildered, till the novice asked leave to speak, and told what he had done to the farmer, and what he had said to Wayland-Smith, and how, though the dormitory light was burning, he had found the wonderful Rune-carved sword in his cot.

'The Abbot shook his head at first, and then he laughed and said to the novice: "Son Hugh, it needed no sign from a heathen God to show me that you will never be a monk. Take your sword, and keep your sword, and go with your sword, and be as gentle as you are strong and courteous. We will hang up the Smith's tools before the Altar," he said, "because, whatever the Smith of the Gods may have been in the old days, we know that he worked honestly for his living and made gifts to Mother Church." Then they went to bed again, all except the novice, and he sat up in the garth playing with his sword. Then Weland said to me by the stables: "Farewell, Old Thing; you had the right of it. You saw me come to England, and you see me go. Farewell!"

'With that he strode down the hill to the corner of the Great Woods – Woods Corner, you call it now – to the very place where he had first landed – and I heard him moving through the thickets towards Horsebridge for a little, and then he was gone. That was how it happened. I saw it.'

Both children drew a long breath.

'But what happened to Hugh the novice?' said Una.

'And the sword?' said Dan.

Puck looked down the meadow that lay all quiet and cool in the shadow of Pook's Hill. A corncrake jarred in a hay-field near by, and the small trouts of the brook began to jump. A big white moth flew unsteadily from the alders and flapped round the children's heads, and the least little haze of water-mist rose from the brook.

'Do you really want to know?' Puck said.

'We do,' cried the children. 'Awfully!'

'Very good. I promised you that you shall see What you shall see, and you shall hear What you shall hear, though It shall have happened three thousand year; but just now it seems to me that, unless you go back to the house, people will be looking for you. I'll walk with you as far as the gate.'

'Will you be here when we come again?' they asked.

'Surely, sure-ly,' said Puck. 'I've been here some time already. One minute first, please.'

He gave them each three leaves – one of Oak, one of Ash and one of Thorn.

'Bite these,' said he. 'Otherwise you might be talking at home of what you've seen and heard, and – if I know human beings – they'd send for the doctor. Bite!'

They bit hard, and found themselves walking side by side to the lower gate. Their father was leaning over it.

'And how did your play go?' he asked.

'Oh, splendidly,' said Dan. 'Only afterwards, I think, we went to sleep. It was very hot and quiet. Don't you remember, Una?'

Una shook her head and said nothing.

'I see,' said her father.

> 'Late – late in the evening Kilmeny came home,
> For Kilmeny had been she could not tell where,
> And Kilmeny had seen what she could not declare.

'But why are you chewing leaves at your time of life, daughter? For fun?'

'No. It was for something, but I can't exactly remember,' said Una.

And neither of them could.

A TREE SONG
(A.D. 1200)

Of all the trees that grow so fair
  Old England to adorn,
Greater are none beneath the Sun
  Than Oak and Ash and Thorn.
Sing Oak and Ash and Thorn, good sirs,
  (All of a Midsummer morn!)
Surely we sing no little thing
  In Oak and Ash and Thorn!

Oak of Clay lived many a day
  Or ever Aeneas began.
Ash of the Loam was a lady at home
  When Brut was an outlaw man.
Thorn of the Down saw New Troy Town
  (From which was London born);
Witness hereby the ancientry
  Of Oak and Ash and Thorn!

Yew that is old in churchyard-mould,
  He breedeth a mighty bow.
Alder for shoes do wise men choose,
  And beech for cups also.
But when ye have killed, and your bowl is spilled,
  And your shoes are clean outworn,
Back ye must speed for all that ye need
  To Oak and Ash and Thorn.

Ellum she hateth mankind, and waiteth
  Till every gust be laid
To drop a limb on the head of him
  That anyway trusts her shade.
But whether a lad be sober or sad,
  Or mellow with ale from the horn,
He will take no wrong when he lieth along
  'Neath Oak and Ash and Thorn!

Oh, do not tell the Priest our plight,
    Or he would call it a sin;
But – we have been out in the woods all night,
    A-conjuring Summer in!
And we bring you news by word of mouth –
    Good news for cattle and corn –
Now is the Sun come up from the South
    With Oak and Ash and Thorn!

Sing Oak and Ash and Thorn, good sirs
    (All of a Midsummer morn!)
England shall bide till Judgement Tide
    By Oak and Ash and Thorn!

Letter to the Reverend Augustus Jessopp, May 16, 1905

> *Dr Jessopp, at this time the rector of Scarning in Norfolk, was the author of several books on medieval England. The stories Kipling refers to here are the three which follow 'Weland's Sword' – 'Young Men at the Manor', 'The Knights of the Joyous Venture' and 'Old Men at Pevensey'.*

All this winter (and before) I have been busy on the adventures of two children who after acting excerpts from *Midsummer Night's Dream* on Midsummer Eve, in the middle of a fairy ring under a fairy hill, most inevitably evoked Puck – the oldest of all old things in old England.

Puck couldn't show 'em any fairies because the fairies have left England but he gave them the Freedom of old England with rather curious results. They met, in their own fields, mounted on his war horse, none other than Sir Richard Dalyngridge who told them by what strange chance he, a few hours after the Battle of Hastings, came to be possessed of the very valley where they sat – in what manner he kept the valley quiet for a year and how he was confirmed in the possession of his manor by the great De Aquila, Lord of the Honour of the Eagle, who held under Mortain who held from William. Also Sir Richard tells them how he by accident in his old age got took by a Dane ship and carried down to the world's end by an Heathen pirate who bought gold from certain folk in Africa who lived in a land of devils. And later he tells them how De Aquila foiled an intrigue to take Pevensey castle from him about the time of the First Henry.

116

All this you will say is skittles. I admit it but I have had a royal time in the doing and I have ploughed with many heifers – not a few from Norfolk. May I send you as much as I have done – there are only four tales – and upon them I pray you, if you will take that trouble, to life up the whip of Discipline and Correction. My notion is to deal only with the portion of Sussex which lies under my own eye, in such manner as, may be, in some day to come, will make the history of our wonderful land a little pleasing to children. Later on I purpose that the children shall meet a legionary from the Roman wall – the last of the soldiers left who fled pursued through the woods to Anderida – and, maybe, some of the old Flint folk who built the dew ponds on Chanctonbury Ring. But at present I have got no further than the 11th century and I fear I am full of errors and blunders. I think it must have been the books you gave me that subconsciously turned me on this path. If there's any good in it I shall feel sure of it.

A Smuggler's Song

If you wake at midnight, and hear a horse's feet,
Don't go drawing back the blind, or looking in the street.
Them that asks no questions isn't told a lie –
Watch the wall, my darling, while the Gentlemen go by!
    Five and twenty ponies
    Trotting through the dark –
    Brandy for the Parson,
    'Baccy for the Clerk;
    Laces for a lady, letters for a spy,
    And watch the wall, my darling, while the Gentlemen go by!

Running round the woodlump if you chance to find
Little barrels, roped and tarred, all full of brandy-wine,
Don't you shout to come and look, nor use 'em for your play.
Put the brishwood back again – and they'll be gone next day!

If you see the stable-door setting open wide;
If you see a tired horse lying down inside;
If your mother mends a coat cut about and tore;
If the lining's wet and warm – don't you ask no more!

If you meet King George's men, dressed in blue and red,
You be careful what you say, and mindful what is said.

If they call you 'pretty maid', and chuck you 'neath the chin,
Don't you tell where no one is, nor yet where no one's been!

Knocks and footsteps round the house – whistles after dark –
You've no call for running out till the house-dogs bark.
Trusty's here, and *Pincher*'s here, and see how dumb they lie –
They don't fret to follow when the Gentlemen go by!

If you do as you've been told, 'likely there's a chance,
You'll be give a dainty doll, all the way from France,
With a cap of Valenciennes, and a velvet hood –
A present from the Gentlemen, along o' being good!
    Five and twenty ponies
    Trotting through the dark –
    Brandy for the Parson,
    'Baccy for the Clerk;
Them that asks no questions isn't told a lie –
Watch the wall, my darling, while the Gentlemen go by!

Kipling inscribed this sundial in the garden at Bateman's with the sombre message 'It's later than you think'.

Rewards and Fairies

With the second book the children are a year or so
older, and now regularly wearing boots instead of going
barefoot. As before, Puck introduces them to characters
from the past and works his magic to take away their
memory of each encounter once it is over.

From 'Something of Myself'

I embarked on *Rewards and Fairies* – the second book – in two minds. Stories a plenty I had to tell, but how many would be authentic and how many due to 'induction'? There was moreover the old Law: 'As soon as you find you can do anything, do something you can't.'

My doubt cleared itself with the first tale, 'Cold Iron', which gave me my underwood: 'What else could I have done?' – the plinth of all structures. Yet, since the tales had to be read by children, before people realised that they were meant for grown-ups; and since they had to be a sort of balance to, as well as a seal upon, some aspects of my 'Imperialistic' output in the past, I worked the material in three or four overlaid tints and textures, which might or might not reveal themselves according to the shifting light of sex, youth and experience. It was like working lacquer and mother-o'-pearl, a natural combination, into the same scheme as niello and grisaille, and trying not to let the joins show.

So I loaded the book up with allegories and allusions, and verified references until my old Chief would have been almost pleased with me; put in three or four really good sets of verses; the bones of one entire historical novel for any to clothe who cared; and even slipped in a cryptogram, whose key I regret I must have utterly forgotten. It was glorious fun; and I knew it must be very good or very bad because the series turned itself off just as Kim had done.

Among the verses in *Rewards* was one set called 'If – ', which escaped from the book, and for a while ran about the world. They were drawn from Jameson's character, and contained counsels of perfection most easy to give. Once started, the mechanisation of the age made them snowball themselves in a way that startled me. Schools, and places where they teach, took them for the suffering Young – which did me no good with the Young when I met them later. ('Why did you write that stuff? I've had to write it out twice as an impot.') They were printed as cards to hang up in offices and bedrooms; illuminated text-wise and anthologised to weariness. Twenty-seven of the Nations of the Earth translated them into their seven-and-twenty tongues, and printed them on every sort of fabric.

If—

The colonial adventurer Dr Leander Starr Jameson, who inspired this poem, visited Kipling at Bateman's in 1910. He had defeated the Matabele in 1893 and led the notorious 'Jameson Raid' into the Transvaal.

If you can keep your head when all about you
  Are losing theirs and blaming it on you,
If you can trust yourself when all men doubt you,
  But make allowance for their doubting too;
If you can wait and not be tired by waiting,
  Or being lied about, don't deal in lies,
Or, being hated, don't give way to hating,
  And yet don't look too good, nor talk too wise:

If you can dream – and not make dreams your master,
  If you can think – and not make thoughts your aim,
If you can meet with Triumph and Disaster
  And treat those two impostors just the same;
If you can bear to hear the truth you've spoken
  Twisted by knaves to make a trap for fools,
Or watch the things you gave your life to, broken,
  And stoop and build 'em up with worn-out tools:

If you can make one heap of all your winnings
  And risk it on one turn of pitch-and-toss,
And lose, and start again at your beginnings
  And never breathe a word about your loss;
If you can force your heart and nerve and sinew
  To serve your turn long after they are gone,
And so hold on when there is nothing in you
  Except the Will which says to them: 'Hold on!'

If you can talk with crowds and keep your virtue,
  Or walk with Kings – nor lose the common touch,
If neither foes nor loving friends can hurt you,
  If all men count with you, but none too much;
If you can fill the unforgiving minute
  With sixty seconds' worth of distance run,
Yours is the Earth and everything that's in it,
  And – which is more – you'll be a Man, my son!

Letter to Edward Lucas White, December 13, 1910
What a lordly appreciation you have sent of *Rewards and Fairies*! I purred when I read it – same as Moses (or Aaron?) did when the ointment ran down 'even to the skirts of his clothing'.

I confess myself to be rather fond of my last baby. In that kind of work one can stuff in, unbeknownst, all manner of allusions and references and cross-references that really don't show up at all unless you hold the texture at a certain angle. At the same time they don't hamper the narrative much. There are angrams and cryptograms in it too, and thefts and plagiarisms and ploughings with other folk's heifers. Yes I did enjoy myself.

THE WAY THROUGH THE WOODS

They shut the road through the woods
Seventy years ago.
Weather and rain have undone it again,
And now you would never know
There was once a road through the woods
Before they planted the trees.
It is underneath the coppice and heath
And the thin anemones.
Only the keeper sees
That, where the ring-dove broods,
And the badgers roll at ease,
There was once a road through the woods.

Yet, if you enter the woods
Of a summer evening late,
When the night-air cools on the trout-ringed pools
Where the otter whistles his mate,
(They fear not men in the woods,
Because they see so few)
You will hear the beat of a horse's feet,
And the swish of a skirt in the dew,
Steadily cantering through
The misty solitudes,
As though they perfectly knew
The old lost road through the woods . . .
But there is no road through the woods.

For this, the fifth of eleven stories in 'Rewards and Fairies', Kipling takes the children back to the 'flint village' of Rottingdean. Ben Dudeney was, indeed, a local shepherd.

The children went to the seaside for a month, and lived in a flint village on the bare windy chalk Downs, quite thirty miles away from home. They made friends with an old shepherd, called Mr Dudeney, who had known their Father when their Father was little. He did not talk like their own people in the Weald of Sussex, and he used different names for farm things, but he understood how they felt, and let them go with him. He had a tiny cottage about half a mile from the village, where his wife made mead from thyme honey, and nursed sick lambs in front of a coal fire, while Old Jim, who was Mr Dudeney's sheep-dog's father, lay at the door. They brought up beef bones for Old Jim (you must never give a sheep-dog mutton bones), and if Mr Dudeney happened to be far in the Downs, Mrs Dudeney would tell the dog to take them to him, and he did.

One August afternoon when the village water-cart had made the street smell specially townified, they went to look for their shepherd as usual, and, as usual, Old Jim crawled over the doorstep and took them in charge. The sun was hot, the dry grass was very slippery, and the distances were very distant.

'It's just like the sea,' said Una, when Old Jim halted in the shade of a lonely flint barn on a bare rise. 'You see where you're going, and – you go there, and there's nothing between.'

Dan slipped off his shoes. 'When we get home I shall sit in the woods all day,' he said.

'Whuff!' said Old Jim, to show he was ready, and struck across a long rolling stretch of turf. Presently he asked for his beefbone.

'Not yet,' said Dan. 'Where's Mr Dudeney? Where's Master?' Old Jim looked as if he thought they were mad, and asked again.

'Don't you give it him,' Una cried. 'I'm not going to be left howling in a desert.'

'Show, boy! Show!' said Dan, for the Downs seemed as bare as the palm of your hand.

Old Jim sighed, and trotted forward. Soon they spied the blob of Mr Dudeney's hat against the sky a long way off.

'Right! All right!' said Dan. Old Jim wheeled round, took his bone carefully between his blunted teeth, and returned to the shadow of the old barn, looking just like a wolf. The children went on. Two kestrels hung bivvering and squealing above them. A gull flapped lazily along the white edge of the cliffs. The curves of the Downs shook a little in the heat, and so did Mr Dudeney's distant head.

They walked toward it very slowly and found themselves staring into a horseshoe-shaped hollow a hundred feet deep, whose steep sides were laced with tangled sheep-tracks. The flock grazed on the flat at the bottom, under charge of Young Jim. Mr Dudeney sat comfortably knitting on the edge of the slope, his crook between his knees. They told him what Old Jim had done.

'Ah, he thought you could see my head as soon as he did. The closer you be to the turf the more you see things. You look warm-like,'said Mr Dudeney.

'We be,' said Una, flopping down. 'And tired.'

'Set beside o' me here. The shadow'll begin to stretch out in a little while, and a heat-shake o' wind will come up with it that'll overlay your eyes like so much wool.'

'We don't want to sleep,' said Una indignantly; but she settled herself as she spoke, in the first strip of early afternoon shade.

'O' course not. You come to talk with me same as your father used. He didn't need no dog to guide him to Norton Pit.'

'Well, he belonged here,' said Dan, and laid himself down at length on the turf.

'He did. And what beats me is why he went off to live among them messy trees in the Weald, when he might ha' stayed here and looked all about him. There's no profit to trees. They draw the lightning, and sheep shelter under 'em, and so, like as not, you'll lose a half-score ewes struck dead in one storm. Tck! Your father knew that.'

'Trees aren't messy.' Una rose on her elbow. 'And what about firewood? I don't like coal.'

'Eh? You lie a piece more uphill and you'll lie more natural,' said Mr Dudeney, with his provoking deaf smile. 'Now press your face down and smell to the turf. That's Southdown thyme which makes our Southdown mutton beyond compare, and, my mother told me, 'twill cure anything except broken necks, or hearts. I forget which.'

They sniffed, and somehow forgot to lift their cheeks from the soft thymy cushions.

'You don't get nothing like that in the Weald. Watercress, maybe?' said Mr Dudeney.

'But we've water – brooks full of it – where you paddle in hot weather,' Una replied, watching a yellow-and-violet-banded snail-shell close to her eye.

'Brooks flood. Then you must shift your sheep – let alone foot-rot afterward. I put more dependence on a dew-pond any day.'

'How's a dew-pond made?' said Dan, and tilted his hat over his eyes. Mr Dudeney explained.

The air trembled a little as though it could not make up its mind whether to slide into the Pit or move across the open. But it seemed easiest to go downhill, and the children felt one soft puff after another slip and sidle down the slope in fragrant breaths that baffed on their eyelids. The little whisper of the sea by the cliffs joined with the whisper of the wind over the grass, the hum of insects in the thyme, the ruffle and rustle of the flock below, and a thickish mutter deep in the very chalk beneath them. Mr Dudeney stopped explaining, and went on with his knitting. They were roused by voices. The shadow had crept halfway down the steep side of Norton Pit, and on the edge of it, his back to them, Puck sat beside a half-naked man who seemed busy at some work. The wind had dropped, and in that funnel of ground every least noise and movement reached them like whispers up a water-pipe.

'That is clever,' said Puck, leaning over. 'How truly you shape it!'

'Yes, but what does The Beast care for a brittle flint tip? Bah!'

Flint mining on the Downs.

The man flicked something contemptuously over his shoulder. It fell between Dan and Una—a beautiful dark-blue flint arrow-head still hot from the maker's hand.

The man reached for another stone, and worked away like a thrush with a snail-shell.

'Flint work is fool's work,' he said at last. 'One does it because one always did it; but when it comes to dealing with The Beast – no good!' He shook his shaggy head.

'The Beast was dealt with long ago. He has gone,' said Puck.

'He'll be back at lambing time. I know him.' He chipped very carefully, and the flints squeaked.

'Not he. Children can lie out on the Chalk now all day through and go home safe.'

'Can they? Well, call The Beast by his True Name, and I'll believe it,' the man replied.

'Surely!' Puck leaped to his feet, curved his hands round his mouth and shouted: 'Wolf! Wolf!'

Norton Pit threw back the echo from its dry sides – 'Wuff!' Wuff!' like Young Jim's bark.

'You see? You hear?' said Puck. 'Nobody answers. Grey Shepherd is gone. Feet-in-the-Night has run off. There are no more wolves.'

'Wonderful!' The man wiped his forehead as though he were hot. 'Who drove him away? You?'

'Many men through many years, each working in his own country. Were you one of them?' Puck answered.

The man slid his sheepskin cloak to his waist, and without a word pointed to his side, which was all seamed and blotched with scars. His arms, too, were dimpled from shoulder to elbow with horrible white dimples.

'I see,' said Puck. 'It is The Beast's mark. What did you use against him?'

'Hand, hammer and spear, as our fathers did before us.'

'So? Then how' – Puck twitched aside the man's dark-brown cloak – 'how did a Flint-worker come by that? Show, man, show!' He held out his little hand.

The man slipped a long dark iron knife, almost a short sword, from his belt, and after breathing on it, handed it hilt-first to Puck, who took it with his head on one side, as you should when you look at the works of a watch, squinted down the dark blade, and very delicately rubbed his forefinger from the point to the hilt.

'Good!' said he, in a surprised tone.

'It should be. The Children of the Night made it,' the man answered.

'So I see by the iron. What might it have cost you?'

'This!' The man raised his hand to his cheek. Puck whistled like a Weald starling.

'By the Great Rings of the Chalk!' he cried. 'Was that your price? Turn sunward that I may see better, and shut your eye.' He slipped his hand beneath the man's chin and swung him till he faced the children up the slope. They saw that his right eye was gone, and the eyelid lay shrunk. Quickly Puck turned him round again, and the two sat down.

'It was for the sheep. The sheep are the people,' said the man, in an ashamed voice. 'What else could I have done? You know, Old One.'

Puck sighed a little fluttering sigh. 'Take the knife. I listen.'

The man bowed his head, drove the knife into the turf, and while it still quivered said: 'This is witness between us that I speak the thing that has been. Before my Knife and the Naked Chalk I speak. Touch!'

Puck laid a hand on the hilt. It stopped shaking. The children wriggled a little nearer.

'I am of the People of the Worked Flint. I am the one son of the Priestess who sells the Winds to the Men of the Sea. I am the Buyer of the Knife – the Keeper of the People,' the man began, in a sort of singing shout. 'These are my names in this country of the Naked Chalk, between the Trees and the Sea.'

'Yours was a great country. Your names are great too,' said Puck.

'One cannot feed some things on names and songs.' The man hit himself on the chest. 'It is better – always better – to count one's children safe round the fire, their Mother among them.'

'Aha!' said Puck. 'I think this will be a very old tale.'

'I warm myself and eat at any fire that I choose, but there is no one to light me a fire or cook my meat. I sold all that when I bought the Magic Knife for my people. It was not right that The Beast should master man. What else could I have done?'

'I hear. I know. I listen,' said Puck.

'When I was old enough to take my place in the Sheepguard, The Beast gnawed all our country like a bone between his teeth. He came in behind the flocks at watering-time, and watched them round the Dew-ponds; he leaped into the folds between our knees at the shearing; he walked out alongside the grazing flocks, and chose his meat on the hoof while our boys threw flints at him; he crept by night into the huts, and licked the babe from between the mother's hands; he called his companions and pulled down men in broad daylight on the Naked Chalk. No – not always did he do so! This was his cunning! He would go away for a while to let us forget him. A year – two years perhaps – we neither smelt, nor heard, nor saw him. When our flocks had increased; when our men did not always look behind them; when children strayed from the fenced places; when our women walked alone to draw water – back, back, back came the Curse of the Chalk, Grey Shepherd, Feet-in-the-Night – The Beast, The Beast, The Beast!

'He laughed at our little brittle arrows and our poor blunt spears. He learned to run in under the stroke of the hammer. I think he knew when there was a flaw in the flint. Often it does not show till you bring it down on his snout. Then – Pouf! – the false flint falls all to flinders, and you are left with the hammer-handle in your fist, and his teeth in your flank! I have felt them. At evening, too, in the dew, or when it has misted and rained, your spear-head lashings slack off, though you have kept them beneath your cloak all day. You are alone – but so close to the home ponds that you stop to tighten the sinews with hands, teeth, and a piece of driftwood. You bend over and pull – so! That is the minute for which he has followed you since the stars went out. "Aarh!" he says. "Wurr-aarh!" he says.' (Norton Pit gave back the growl like a pack of real wolves.) 'Then he is on your right shoulder feeling for the vein in your neck, and – perhaps your sheep run on without you. To fight The Beast is nothing, but to be despised by The Beast when he fights you – that is like his teeth in the heart! Old One, why is it that men desire so greatly, and can do so little?'

'I do not know. Did you desire so much?' said Puck.

'I desired to master The Beast. It is not right that The Beast should master man. But my people were afraid. Even, my Mother, the Priestess, was afraid when I told her what I desired. We were accustomed to be afraid of The Beast. When I was made a man, and a maiden – she was a Priestess – waited for me at the Dew-ponds, The Beast flitted from off the Chalk. Perhaps it was a sickness; perhaps he had gone to his Gods to learn how to do us new harm. But he went, and we breathed more freely. The women sang again; the children were not so much guarded; our flocks grazed far out. I took mine yonder' – he pointed inland to the hazy line of the Weald – 'where the new grass was best. They grazed north. I followed till we were close to the Trees' – he lowered his voice – 'close there where the Children of the Night live.' He pointed north again.

'Ah, now I remember a thing,' said Puck. 'Tell me, why did your people fear the Trees so extremely?'

'Because the Gods hate the Trees and strike them with lightning. We can see them burning for days all along the Chalk's edge. Besides, all the Chalk knows that the Children of the Night, though they worship our Gods, are magicians. When a man goes into their country, they change his spirit; they put words into his mouth; they make him like talking water. But a voice in my heart told me to go toward the north. While I watched my sheep there I saw three Beasts chasing a man, who ran toward the Trees. By this I knew he was a Child of the Night. We Flint-workers fear the Trees more than we fear The Beast. He had no hammer. He carried a knife like this one. A Beast leaped at him. He stretched out his knife. The Beast fell dead. The other Beasts ran away howling, which they would never have done from a Flint-worker. The man went in among the Trees. I looked for the dead Beast. He had been killed in a new way – by a single deep, clean cut, without bruise or tear, which had split his bad heart. Wonderful! So I saw that the man's knife was magic, and I thought how to get it – thought strongly how to get it.

'When I brought the flocks to the shearing, my Mother the Priestess asked me, "What is the new thing which you have seen and I see in your face?" I said, "It is a sorrow to me"; and she answered, "All new things are sorrow. Sit in my place, and eat sorrow." I sat down in her place by the fire, where she talks to the ghosts in winter, and two voices spoke in my heart. One voice said, "Ask the Children of the Night for the Magic Knife. It is not fit that The Beast should master man." I listened to that voice.

'One voice said, "If you go among the Trees, the Children of the Night will change your spirit. Eat and sleep here." The other voice said, "Ask for the Knife." I listened to that voice.

'I said to my Mother in the morning, "I go away to find a thing for the people, but I do not know whether I shall return in my own shape." She answered, "Whether you live or die, or are made different, I am your Mother."'

'True,' said Puck. 'The Old Ones themselves cannot change men's mothers even if they would.'

'Let us thank the Old Ones! I spoke to my Maiden, the Priestess who waited for me at the Dew-ponds. She promised fine things too.' The man laughed. 'I went away to that place where I had seen the magician with the knife. I lay out two days on the short grass before I ventured among the Trees. I felt my way before me with a stick. I was afraid of the terrible talking Trees. I was afraid of the ghosts in the branches; of the soft ground underfoot; of the red and black waters. I was afraid, above all, of the Change. It came!'

They saw him wipe his forehead once again, and his strong back-muscles quivered till he laid his hand on the knife-hilt.

'A fire without a flame burned in my head; an evil taste grew in my mouth; my eyelids shut hot over my eyes; my breath was hot between my teeth, and my hands were like the hands of a stranger. I was made to sing songs and to mock the Trees, though I was afraid of them. At the same time I saw myself laughing, and I was very sad for this fine young man, who was myself. Ah! The Children of the Night know magic.'

'I think that is done by the Spirits of the Mist. They change a man, if he sleeps among them,' said Puck. 'Had you slept in any mists?'

'Yes – but I know it was the Children of the Night. After three days I saw a red light behind the Trees, and I heard a heavy noise. I saw the Children of the Night dig red stones from a hole, and lay them in fires. The stones melted like tallow, and the men beat the soft stuff with hammers. I wished to speak to these men, but the words were changed in my mouth, and all I could say was, "Do not make that noise. It hurts my head." By this I knew that I was bewitched, and I clung to the Trees, and prayed the Children of the Night to take off their spells. They were cruel. They asked me many questions which they would never allow me to answer. They changed my words between my teeth till I wept. Then they led me into a hut and covered the floor with hot stones and dashed water on the stones, and sang charms till the sweat poured off me like water. I slept. When I waked, my own spirit – not the strange, shouting thing – was back in my body, and I was like a cool bright stone on the shingle between the sea and the sunshine. The magicians came to hear me – women and men – each wearing a Magic Knife. Their Priestess was their Ears and their Mouth.

'I spoke. I spoke many words that went smoothly along like sheep in order when their shepherd, standing on a mound, can count those coming, and those far off getting ready to come. I asked for Magic Knives for my people. I said that my people would bring meat, and milk, and wool, and lay them in the short grass outside the Trees, if the Children of the Night would leave Magic Knives for our people to take away. They were pleased. Their Priestess said, "For whose sake have you come?" I answered, "The sheep are the people. If The Beast kills our sheep, our people die. So I come for a Magic Knife to kill The Beast."

'She said, "We do not know if our God will let us trade with the people of the Naked Chalk. Wait till we have asked."

'When they came back from the Question-place (their Gods are our Gods), their Priestess said, "The God needs a proof that your words are true." I said, "What is the proof?" She said, "The God says that if you have come for the sake of your people you will give him your right eye to be put out; but if you have come for any other reason you will not give it. This proof is between you and the God. We ourselves are sorry."

'I said, "This is a hard proof. Is there no other road?"

'She said, "Yes. You can go back to your people with your two eyes in your head if you choose. But then you will not get any Magic Knives for your people."

'I said, "It would be easier if I knew that I were to be killed."

'She said, "Perhaps the God knew this too. See! I have made my knife hot."

'I said, "Be quick, then!" With her knife heated in the flame she put out my right eye. She herself did it. I am the son of a Priestess. She was a Priestess. It was not work for any common man.'

'True! Most true,' said Puck. 'No common man's work that. And, afterwards?'

'Afterwards I did not see out of that eye any more. I found also that a one eye does not tell you truly where things are. Try it!'

At this Dan put his hand over one eye, and reached for the flint arrow-head on the grass. He missed it by inches. 'It's true,' he whispered to Una. 'You can't judge distances a bit with only one eye.'

Puck was evidently making the same experiment, for the man laughed at him.

'I know it is so,' said he. 'Even now I am not always sure of my blow. I stayed with the Children of the Night till my eye healed. They said I was the son of Tyr, the God who put his right hand in a Beast's mouth. They showed me how they melted their red stone and made the Magic Knives of it. They told me the charms they sang over the fires and at the beatings. I can sing many charms.' Then he began to laugh like a boy.

'I was thinking of my journey home,' he said, 'and of the surprised Beast. He had come back to the Chalk. I saw him – I smelt his lairs as soon as ever I left the Trees. He did not know I had the Magic Knife – I hid it under my cloak—the Knife that the Priestess gave me. Ho! Ho! That happy day was too short! See! A Beast would wind me. "Wow!" he would say. "Here is my Flint-worker!" He would come leaping, tail in air; he would roll; he would lay his head between his paws out of merriness of heart at his warm, waiting meal. He would leap – and, oh, his eye in mid-leap when he saw – when he saw the knife held ready for him! It pierced his hide as a rush pierces curdled milk. Often he had no time to howl. I did not trouble to flay any beasts I killed. Sometimes I missed my blow. Then I took my little flint hammer and beat out his brains as he cowered. He made no fight. He knew the Knife! But The Beast is very cunning. Before evening all The Beasts had smelt the blood on my knife, and were running from me like hares. They knew! Then I walked as a man should—the Master of The Beast!

'So came I back to my Mother's house. There was a lamb to be killed. I cut it in two halves with my knife, and I told her all my tale. She said, "This is the work of a God." I kissed her and laughed. I went to my Maiden who waited for me at the Dew-ponds. There was a lamb to be killed. I cut it in two halves with my knife, and told her all my tale. She said, "It is the work of a God." I laughed, but she pushed me away, and being on my blind side, ran off before I could kiss her. I went to the Men of the Sheepguard at watering-time. There was a sheep to be killed for their meat. I cut it in two halves with my knife, and told them all my tale. They said, "It is the work of a God." I said, "We talk too much about Gods. Let us eat and be happy, and tomorrow I will take you to the Children of the Night, and each man will find a Magic Knife."

'I was glad to smell our sheep again; to see the broad sky from edge to edge, and to hear the sea. I slept beneath the stars in my cloak. The men talked among themselves.

'I led them, the next day, to the Trees, taking with me meat, wool, and curdled milk, as I had promised. We found the Magic Knives laid out on the grass, as the Children of the Night had promised. They watched us from among the Trees. Their Priestess called to me and said, "How is it with your people?" I said "Their hearts are changed. I cannot see their hearts as I used to." She said, "That is because you have only one eye. Come to me and I will be both your eyes." But I said, "I must show my people how to use their knives against The Beast, as you showed me how to use my knife." I said this because the Magic Knife does not balance like the flint. She said, "What you have done, you have done for the sake of a woman, and not for the sake of your people." I asked of her, "Then why did the God accept my right eye, and why are you so angry?" She answered, "Because any man can lie to a God, but no man can lie to a woman. And I am not angry with you. I am only very sorrowful for you. Wait a little, and you will see out of your one eye why I am sorry. So she hid herself.

'I went back with my people, each one carrying his Knife, and making it sing in the air – tssee-sssse. The Flint never sings. It mutters – ump-ump. The Beast heard. The Beast saw. He knew! Everywhere he ran away from us. We all laughed. As we walked over the grass my Mother's brother – the Chief on the Men's Side – he took off his Chief's necklace of yellow sea-stones.'

'How? Eh? Oh, I remember! Amber,' said Puck.

'And would have put them on my neck. I said, "No, I am content. What does my one eye matter if my other eye sees fat sheep and fat children running about safely?" My Mother's brother said to them, "I told you he would never take such things." Then they began to sing a song in the Old Tongue—The Song of Tyr. I sang with them, but my Mother's brother said, "This is your song, O Buyer of the Knife. Let us sing it, Tyr."

'Even then I did not understand, till I saw that – that no man stepped on my shadow; and I knew that they thought me to be a God, like the God Tyr, who gave his right hand to conquer a Great Beast.'

'By the Fire in the Belly of the Flint was that so?' Puck rapped out.

'By my Knife and the Naked Chalk, so it was! They made way for my shadow as though it had been a Priestess walking to the Barrows of the Dead. I was afraid. I said to myself, "My Mother and my Maiden will know I am not Tyr." But still I was afraid, with the fear of a man who falls into a steep flint-pit while he runs, and feels that it will be hard to climb out.

'When we came to the Dew-ponds all our people were there. The men showed their knives and told their tale. The sheep guards also had seen The Beast flying from us. The Beast went west across the river in packs – howling! He knew the Knife had come to the Naked Chalk at last – at last! He knew! So my work was done. I looked for my Maiden among the Priestesses. She looked at me, but she did not smile. She made the sign to me that our Priestesses must make when they sacrifice to the Old Dead in the Barrows. I would have spoken, but my Mother's brother made himself my Mouth, as though I had been one of the Old Dead in the Barrows for whom our Priests speak to the people on Midsummer Mornings.'

'I remember. Well I remember those Midsummer Mornings!' said Puck.

'Then I went away angrily to my Mother's house. She would have knelt before me. Then I was more angry, but she said, "Only a God would have spoken to me thus, a Priestess. A man would have feared the punishment of the Gods." I looked at her and I laughed. I could not stop my unhappy laughing. They called me from the door by the name of Tyr himself. A young man with whom I had watched my first flocks, and chipped my first arrow, and fought my first Beast, called me by that name in the Old Tongue. He asked my leave to take my Maiden. His eyes were lowered, his hands were on his forehead. He was full of the fear of a God, but of me, a man, he had no fear when he asked. I did not kill him. I said, "Call the maiden." She came also without fear – this very one that had waited for me, that had talked with me, by our Dew-ponds. Being a Priestess, she lifted her eyes to me. As I look on a hill or a cloud, so she looked at me. She spoke in the Old Tongue which Priestesses use when they make prayers to the Old Dead in the Barrows. She asked leave that she might light the fire in my companion's house – and that I should bless their children. I did not kill her. I heard my own voice, little and cold, say, "Let it be as you desire," and they went away hand in hand. My heart grew little and cold; a wind shouted in my ears; my eye darkened. I said to my Mother, "Can a God die?" I heard her say, "What is it? What is it, my son?" and I fell into darkness full of hammer-noises. I was not.'

'Oh, poor – poor God!' said Puck. 'And your wise Mother?'

'She knew. As soon as I dropped she knew. When my spirit came back I heard her whisper in my ear, "Whether you live or die, or are made different, I am your Mother." That was good – better even than the water she gave me and the going away of the sickness. Though I was ashamed to have fallen down, yet I was very glad. She was glad too. Neither of us wished to lose the other. There is only the one Mother for the one son. I heaped the fire for her, and barred the doors, and sat at her feet as before I went away, and she combed my hair, and sang.

'I said at last, "What is to be done to the people who say that I am Tyr?"

'She said, "He who has done a God-like thing must bear himself like a God. I see no way out of it. The people are now your sheep till you die. You cannot drive them off."

'I said, "This is a heavier sheep than I can lift." She said, "In time it will grow easy. In time perhaps you will not lay it down for any maiden anywhere. Be wise—be very wise, my son, for nothing is left you except the words, and the songs, and the worship of a God."

'Oh, poor God!' said Puck. 'But those are not altogether bad things.'

'I know they are not; but I would sell them all – all – all for one small child of my own, smearing himself with the ashes of our own house-fire.'

He wrenched his knife from the turf, thrust it into his belt and stood up.

'And yet, what else could I have done?' he said. 'The sheep are the people.'

'It is a very old tale,' Puck answered. 'I have heard the like of it not only on the Naked Chalk, but also among the Trees – under Oak, and Ash and Thorn.'

The afternoon shadows filled all the quiet emptiness of Norton Pit. The children heard the sheep-bells and Young Jim's busy bark above them, and they scrambled up the slope to the level.

'We let you have your sleep out,' said Mr Dudeney, as the flock scattered before them. 'It's making for tea-time now.'

'Look what I've found, said Dan, and held up a little blue flint arrow-head as fresh as though it had been chipped that very day.

'Oh,' said Mr Dudeney, 'the closer you be to the turf the more you're apt to see things. I've found 'em often. Some says the fairies made 'em, but I says they was made by folks like ourselves – only a goodish time back. They're lucky to keep. Now, you couldn't ever have slept – not to any profit – among your father's trees same as you've laid out on Naked Chalk – could you?'

'One doesn't want to sleep in the woods,' said Una.

'Then what's the good of 'em?' said Mr Dudeney. 'Might as well set in the barn all day. Fetch 'em 'long, Jim boy!'

The Downs, that looked so bare and hot when they came, were full of delicious little shadow-dimples; the smell of the thyme and the salt mixed together on the south-west drift from the still sea; their eyes dazzled with the low sun, and the long grass under it looked golden. The sheep knew where their fold was, so Young Jim came back to his master, and they all four strolled home, the scabious-heads swishing about their ankles, and their shadows streaking behind them like the shadows of giants.

EDDI'S SERVICE
(A.D. 687)

*The exiled northern bishop St Wilfrid, who kick-started
the conversion of Sussex to Christianity, founded a
monastery at Selsey on land now covered by the sea.
The area is known as the Manhood Peninsula.*

Eddi, priest of St Wilfrid
  In his chapel at Manhood End,
Ordered a midnight service
  For such as cared to attend.

But the Saxons were keeping Christmas,
  And the night was stormy as well.
Nobody came to service,
  Though Eddi rang the bell.

'Wicked weather for walking,'
  Said Eddi of Manhood End.
'But I must go on with the service
  For such as care to attend.'

The altar lamps were lighted –
  An old marsh-donkey came,
Bold as a guest invited,
  And stared at the guttering flame.

The storm beat on at the windows,
  The water splashed on the floor,
And a wet, yoke-weary bullock
  Pushed in through the open door.

'How do I know what is greatest,
  How do I know what is least?
That is My Father's business,'
  Said Eddi, Wilfrid's priest.

'But – three are gathered together –
  Listen to me and attend.
I bring good news, my brethren!'
  Said Eddi of Manhood End.

And he told the Ox of a Manger
  And a Stall in Bethlehem,
And he spoke to the Ass of a Rider
  That rode to Jerusalem.

They steamed and dripped in the chancel,
  They listened and never stirred,
While, just as though they were Bishops,
  Eddi preached them The Word.

Till the gale blew off on the marshes
  And the windows showed the day,
And the Ox and the Ass together
  Wheeled and clattered away.

And when the Saxons mocked him,
  Said Eddi of Manhood End,
'I dare not shut His chapel
  On such as care to attend.'

The avenue of pleached limes had already been planted before the Kiplings arrived at Bateman's, but they created the formal garden with its pond. The children and friends enjoyed paddling about in a small boat, and the visitors' book occasionally adds the letters FIP to a name: 'Fell in pond.'

Thanks for your two letters about *Rewards and Fairies*. I think I never had more pure fun over a yarn . . . But don't give the show away. I specially don't want people to notice my 'style'. All I want is to get the medium as little insistent as possible, and the minute the reader begins to look at the glass instead of through it the game is up. But as you say, it's a nice game to play.

THE RUN OF THE DOWNS

The Weald is good, the Downs are best –
I'll give you the run of 'em, East to West.
Beachy Head and Winddoor Hill,
They were once and they are still.
Firle, Mount Caburn and Mount Harry
Go back as far as sums'll carry.
Ditchling Beacon and Chanctonbury Ring,
They have looked on many a thing,
And what those two have missed between 'em,
I reckon Truleigh Hill has seen 'em.
Highden, Bignor and Duncton Down
Knew Old England before the Crown.
Linch Down, Treyford and Sunwood
Knew Old England before the Flood;
And when you end on the Hampshire side –
Butser's old as Time and Tide.
The Downs are sheep, the Weald is corn,
You be glad you are Sussex born!

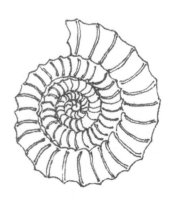

THE LAND AND THE PEOPLE

After the first world war life was never the same for the Kiplings. They had now lost two of their three children, and when Elsie married in 1924 they felt bereft. Politically Kipling seemed ever further adrift from the mainstream, to such an extent that he regarded his once-close cousin Stanley Baldwin, who became Conservative prime minister in 1923, as 'a Socialist at heart'. Old friends such as Rider Haggard died, and his increasingly boorish demeanour meant that he made few new ones. He fell out with Lionel Dunsterville, the model for 'Stalky' in his school stories, for becoming president of the newly-formed Kipling Society and giving talks about him – an unpardonable intrusion on his precious privacy.

Of course he continued to write, and he produced two further collections of stories, 'Debits and Credits' (1926) and 'Limits and Renewals' (1932). Now, though, there were as many pot-boilers as first-class works, among them *The Irish Guards in the Great War* (with his son earning a passing reference) and *Land and Sea Tales for Scouts and Guides* (Baden-Powell was a long-standing friend).

The spartan atmosphere at Bateman's has already been noted, and the hospitality now began to be of a piece with the ambience. It would be easy to compile an impressive list of the great and the good who stayed at Bateman's over the years, and Kipling was a lively man in company. Carrie, however, grew ever more off-putting to visitors, more parsimonious and more protective of her husband. (A portrait by Philip Burne-Jones, which hangs in the study at Bateman's, shows her with the household keys symbolically at her waist.) In her defence it should be said that she suffered recurrent bouts of depression, and that Kipling's health had never been robust. From around 1915 he suffered severe stomach pains, which he believed signalled cancer, a lifetime's dread: in fact they were caused by the duodenal ulcers which eventually claimed his life.

They continued to travel (turning off the electricity when they went, and counting out the candles and matches to the servants they left behind). With George V they visited war cemeteries on the continent, and they took winter holidays around the Mediterranean and motor tours in France – although even that pleasure was marred for him by the increasing press of traffic on the roads. Later they visited Rio de Janeiro, Bermuda, Canada and (their last holiday) Marienbad.

During my early years with the BBC in Sussex I interviewed people who had worked for the family, and the consensus was that Kipling had been a decent but distant employer, while his wife was severe and to be avoided. On one occasion, I was told, she had visited a team of workers by the mill pond and by chance stood on the end of a plank which lay in the grass. A labourer standing on the other end of it smartly stepped away, so that she was pitched into the water. Although impossible to verify, the tale speaks a truth about her reputation among the kind of ordinary country folk for whom Kipling had considerable respect.

About Sussex and its people (or, at least, those amenable to the myth he created for them), he had no doubts. When he read Fletcher's draft of the history they were collaborating on he urged him to give more stress to 'the spirit of the land'. In the short story *An Habitation Enforced* a rich American couple buy an ancient Sussex estate and find themselves tamed by that timeless spirit. When George Chapin considers closing a public right of way his wife tells him that it is impossible. He protests:

> 'But it's our land. We can do what we like.'
> 'It's not our land. We've only paid for it. We belong to it, and it belongs to the people – our people, they call 'em.'

The archetypal countryman is old Hobden, a hedger in the Puck stories but only the latest in a long line of village Hobdens who have given the benefit of their folk wisdom to the land that created them. ('Clay of the pit whence we were wrought/Yearns to its fellow-clay,' he had written in 'Sussex'.) It's a myth which can easily slip through the fingers, but his espousal of it surely gave Kipling, always the outsider, a longed-for sense of rootedness.

A Charm

Take of English earth as much
As either hand may rightly clutch.
In the taking of it breathe
Prayer for all who lie beneath.
Not the great nor well-bespoke,
But the more uncounted folk
Of whose life and death is none
Report or lamentation.
   Lay that earth upon thy heart,
   And thy sickness shall depart!

It shall sweeten and make whole
Fevered breath and festered soul.
It shall mightily restrain
Over-busied hand and brain.
It shall ease thy mortal strife
'Gainst the immortal woe of life,
Till thyself, restored, shall prove
By what grace the Heavens do move.

Take of English flowers these –
Spring's full-facèd primroses,
Summer's wild wide-hearted rose,
Autumn's wall-flower of the close,
And, thy darkness to illume,
Winter's bee-thronged ivy-bloom.
Seek and serve them where they bide
From Candlemas to Christmas-tide,
   For these simples used aright
   Can restore a failing sight.

These shall cleanse and purify
Webbed and inward-turning eye;
These shall show thee treasure hid
Thy familiar fields amid;
And reveal (which is thy need)
Every man a King indeed!

Letter to Edmonia Hill, October 23–November 11, 1905
We've been having a fortnight of clear white morning frosts – rather like the cold weather in India – changing to soft hazy days sometimes, but most generally with a bitter tooth of edged east wind running through the sunshine. I suppose east winds are healthy but they cut like knives.

This is the time on the 'farms' for putting hedges in order and for sawing timber and for planting new trees. These matters are attended to by primitive Anglo-Saxons with blue eyes and light hair who emerge from their hiding places in due season and who remind me at a hundred points of the North Western raiyat [farmer]. Shrewd men of curious simplicity and still more curious calculations: silent (except among themselves) secretive; observant and skilled in their craft.

I don't know whether they like me but some of them behave as if they did. One of them has a butter-nut in his garden. His brother brought the seed over ten years ago and the man set himself to plant and grow it. Now it is a little tree – still unused to our English climate. It expects summer after winter instead of our spring; and as poor Morris says 'It's them snigglin' May frosteses that terrifies her nigh to death.' Poor little beast! He looks after her with great care and straws her up when cold threatens. I wanted to buy it but Morris won't (and I respect it) part with 'her' – except to the Church where he is sure that once planted no one will molest 'her'.

Well-head by the mill at Bateman's.

THE RECALL

*This poem appears in Kipling's short story collection
'Actions and Reactions'*

I am the land of their fathers.
In me the virtue stays.
I will bring back my children,
After certain days.

Under their feet in the grasses
My clinging magic runs.
They shall return as strangers,
They shall remain as sons.

Over their heads in the branches
Of their new-bought, ancient trees,
I weave an incantation
And draw them to my knees.

Scent of smoke in the evening,
Smell of rain in the night –
The hours, the days and the seasons,
Order their souls aright,

Till I make plain the meaning
Of all my thousand years –
Till I fill their hearts with knowledge,
While I fill their eyes with tears.

Letter to Josephine Dunham, October 21, 1910
A wet, warm cloudy day of disconnected spurts of rain and bands of mist
– cold inside the house with the cold of damp – but as hot outside as an
August day. And Carrie and I have just come in from a tramp through
the moist fields. I don't know whether you know that C. has recently
bought a 24 acre farm – six acres of which are in fruit trees – apple,
plum, pear, cherries, gooseberries, rasps and currants with a little house,
barn and stable. [The Orchards at Rye Green, a little to the west of
Bateman's.] These latter things she has had painted, papered, tarred and
so forth and has rented the place to the Rector's gardener – a sallow,
shrewd gipsy-faced man married to a rather New-England-school-marm-

like wife who wears pince-nez and is an expert at bringing up young chickens in the way they should go – to market. Incidentally the farm lacked many gates and gate-posts and for weeks past C. and I go up there (it is two hundred feet higher than we are) and watch the extremely leisurely work of an aged English rustic, who makes gates. Law! How Wolcott would have rejoiced in that rustic! In aspect he is like a dried apple; in speech he is, unless you know the Sussex tongue, perfectly unintelligible, but he is a mine of wisdom about trees, hedges, plants and the Earth generally. He moves somewhat quicker than the hour hand of a watch but he never stops working and is serenely indifferent to any weather.

We found him today, with a bit of sackcloth over his shoulders, to keep out the worst of the wet, shovelling dirt into a post hole. He regarded us, even as a tortoise might regard us, pointed out that it was wet and sternly went on with his job. Gates, by the way, are merely a side-issue of his life. His real work is to cut down and then grub out three hundred yards of ancient, gnarled and thorny English hedge which stands on a bank separating two fields that C. wishes to be thrown into one. To watch that little bent back confronting such a gigantic job and – which is more wonderful – making an impression on it, gives one a new respect for mankind.

The Land

When Julius Fabricius, Sub-Prefect of the Weald,
In the days of Diocletian owned our Lower River-field,
He called to him Hobdenius – a Briton of the Clay,
Saying: 'What about that River-piece for layin' in to hay?'

And the aged Hobden answered: 'I remember as a lad
My father told your father that she wanted dreenin' bad.
An' the more that you neglect her the less you'll get her clean.
Have it jest *as* you've a mind to, but, if I was you, I'd dreen.'

So they drained it long and crossways in the lavish Roman style –
Still we find among the river-drift their flakes of ancient tile,
And in drouthy middle August, when the bones of meadows show,
We can trace the lines they followed sixteen hundred years ago.

Then Julius Fabricius died as even Prefects do,
And after certain centuries, Imperial Rome died too.

Then did robbers enter Britain from across the Northern main
And our Lower River-field was won by Ogier the Dane.

Well could Ogier work his war-boat – well could Ogier wield his brand –
Much he knew of foaming waters – not so much of farming land.
So he called to him a Hobden of the old unaltered blood,
Saying: 'What about that River-piece, she doesn't look no good.'

And that aged Hobden answered: "Tain't for *me* to interfere,
But I've known that bit o' meadow now for five and fifty year.
Have it *jest* as you've a mind to, but I've proved it time on time,
If you want to change her nature you have got to give her lime!'

Ogier sent his wains to Lewes, twenty hours' solemn walk,
And drew back great abundance of the cool, grey healing chalk.
And old Hobden spread it broadcast, never heeding what was in't –
Which is why in cleaning ditches, now and then we find a flint.

Ogier died. His sons grew English – Anglo-Saxon was their name –
Till out of blossomed Normandy another pirate came;
For Duke William conquered England and divided with his men,
And our Lower River-field he gave to William of Warenne.

But the Brooke (you know her habit) rose one rainy autumn night
And tore down sodden flitches of the bank to left and right.
So, said William to his Bailiff as they rode their dripping rounds:
'Hob, what about that River-bit – the Brook's got up no bounds?'

And that aged Hobden answered: "Tain't my business to advise,
But ye might ha' known 'twould happen from the way the valley lies.
Where he can't hold back the water you must try and save the sile.
Hev it jest as you've a *mind* to, but, if I was you, I'd spile!'

They spiled along the water-course with trunks of willow-trees,
And planks of elms behind 'em and immortal oaken knees.
And when the spates of Autumn whirl the gravel-beds away
You can see their faithful fragments, iron-hard in iron clay.

Georgii Quinti Anno Sexto, I, who own the River-field,
Am fortified with title-deeds, attested, signed and sealed,

Guaranteeing me, my assigns, my executors and heirs
All sorts of powers and profits which – are neither mine nor theirs.

I have rights of chase and warren, as my dignity requires.
I can fish – but Hobden tickles. I can shoot – but Hobden wires.
I repair, but he reopens, certain gaps which, men allege,
Have been used by every Hobden since a Hobden swapped a hedge.

Shall I dog his morning progress o'er the track-betraying dew?
Demand his dinner-basket into which my pheasants flew?
Confiscate his evening faggot under which my conies ran,
And summon him to judgement? I would sooner summons Pan.

His dead are in the churchyard – thirty generations laid.
Their names were old in history when Domesday Book was made;
And the passion and the piety and prowess of his line
Have seeded, rooted, fruited in some land the Law calls mine.

Nor for any beast that burrows, nor for any bird that flies,
Would I lose his large sound counsel, miss his keen amending eyes.
He is bailiff, woodman, wheelwright, field-surveyor, engineer,
And if flagrantly a poacher – 'tain't for me to interfere.

'Hob, what about that River-bit?' I turn to him again,
With Fabricius and Ogier and William of Warenne.
'Hev is jest as you've a mind to, *but*,' – and here he takes command.
For whoever pays the taxes old Mus' Hobden owns the land.

From 'Something of Myself'

There was one among them, close upon seventy when we first met, a poacher by heredity and instict, a gentleman who, when his need to drink was on him, which was not too often, absented himself and had it out alone; and he was more 'one with Nature' than whole parlours full of poets. He became our special stay and counsellor.

Once we wanted to shift a lime and a witch-elm into the garden proper. He said not a word till we talked of getting a tree-specialist from London. 'Have it as you're minded. I dunno as I should if I was you,' was his comment. By this we understood that he would take charge when the planets were favourable. Presently, he called up four of his own kind (also artists) and brushed us aside. The trees came away kindly. He placed them, with due regard for their growth for the next two or three generations; supported them, throat and bole, with stays and stiffenings, and bade us hold them thus for four years. All fell out as he had foretold. The trees are now close on forty foot high and have never flinched. Equally, a well-grown witch-elm that needed discipline, he climbed into and topped, and she carries to this day the graceful dome he gave her. In his later years – he lived to be close on eighty-five – he would, as I am doing now, review his past, which held incident enough for many unpublishable volumes. He spoke of old loves, fights, intrigues, anonymous denunciations 'by such folk as knew writing', and vindictive conspiracies carried out with oriental thoroughness.

Of poaching he talked in all its branches, from buying *Cocculus indicus* for poisoning fish in ponds, to the art of making silk-nets for trout-brooks – mine among them, and he left a speciment to me; and of pitched battles (guns barred) with heavy-handed keepers in the old days in Lord Ashburnham's woods where a man might pick up a fallow deer. His sagas were lighted with pictures of Nature as he, indeed, knew her; night-pieces and dawn-breakings; stealthy returns and the thinking out of alibis, all naked by the fire, while his clothes dried; and of the face and temper of the next twilight under which he stole forth to follow his passion. His wife, after she had known us for ten years, would range through a past that accepted magic, witchcraft and love-philtres, for which last there was a demand as late as the middle sixties.

She described one midnight ritual at the local 'wise woman's' cottage, when a black cock was killed with curious rites and words, and 'all de time dere was, like, someone trying to come through at ye from outside in de dark. Dunno as I believe so much in such things now, but when I was a maid I – I justabout did!' She died well over ninety, and to the last carried the tact, manner and presence, for all she was so small, of an old-world Duchess.

ALNASCHAR AND THE OXEN

*Here's a poem (included in the short story collection
'Debits and Credits') by Kipling the proud farmer. He
may have been no Lobengula, as he admits, but he did
own twenty-six of the lovely red Sussex cattle.*

There's a pasture in a valley where the hanging woods divide,
    And a Herd lies down and ruminates in peace;
Where the pheasant rules the nooning, and the owl the twilight-tide,
    And the war-cries of our world die out and cease.
Here I cast aside the burden that each weary week-day brings
    And, delivered from the shadows I pursue,
On peaceful, postless Sabbaths I consider Weighty Things –
    Such as Sussex Cattle feeding in the dew!

At the gate beside the river where the trouty shallows brawl,
    I know the pride that Lobengula felt,
When he bade the bars be lowered of the Royal Cattle Kraal,
    And fifteen miles of oxen took the veldt.
From the walls of Bulawayo in unbroken file they came
    To where the Mount of Council cuts the blue . . .
I have only six and twenty, but the principle's the same
    With my Sussex Cattle feeding in the dew!

To a luscious sound of tearing, where the clovered herbage rips,
    Level-backed and level-bellied watch 'em move –
See those shoulders, guess that heart-girth, praise those loins, admire
        those hips,
    And the tail set low for flesh to make above!
Count the broad unblemished muzzles, test the kindly mellow skin,
    And, where yon heifer lifts her head at call,
Mark the bosom's just abundance 'neath the gay and clean-cut chin,
    And those eyes of Juno, overlooking all!

146

Here is colour, form and substance! I will put it to the proof
    And, next season, in my lodges shall be born
Some very Bull of Mithras, flawless from his agate hoof
    To his even-branching, ivory, dusk-tipped horn.
He shall mate with block-square virgins – kings shall seek his like in vain,
    While I multiply his stock a thousandfold,
Till an hungry world extol me, builder of a lofty strain
    That turns one standard ton at two years old!

There's a valley, under oakwood, where a man may dream his dream,
    In the milky breath of cattle laid at ease,
Till the moon o'ertops the alders, and her image chills the stream,
    And the river-mist runs silver round their knees!
Now the footpaths fade and vanish; now the ferny clumps deceive;
    Now the hedgerow-folk possess their fields anew;
Now the Herd is lost in darkness, and I bless them as I leave,
    My Sussex Cattle feeding in the dew!

From 'Something of Myself'
There were interesting and helpful outsiders, too. One was a journeyman
bricklayer who, I remember, kept a store of gold sovereigns loose in his
pocket, and kindly built us a wall; but so leisurely that he came to be
almost part of the establishment.

When we wished to sink a well opposite some cottages, he said he had
the gift of water-finding, and I testify that, when he held one fork of the
hazel Y and I the other, the thing bowed itself against all the grip of my
hand over an unfailing supply.

Then, out of the woods that know everything and tell nothing, came
two dark and mysterious Primitives. They had heard. They would sink
that well, for they had the 'gift'. Their tools were an enormous wooden
trug, a portable windlass whose handles were curved, and smooth as
ox-horns, and a short-handled hoe. They made a ring of brickwork on
the bare ground and, with their hands at first, grubbed out the dirt
beneath it. As the ring sank they heightened it, course by course, grubbing
out with the hoe, till the shaft, true as a rifle-barrel, was deep enough to
call for their Father of Trugs, which one brother down below would fill,
and the other haul up on the magic windlass. When we stopped, at
twenty-five feet, we had found a Jacobean tobacco-pipe, a worn
Cromwellian latten spoon and, at the bottom of all, the bronze cheek of
a Roman horse-bit.

Norman and Saxon
(A.D. 1100)

'My son,' said the Norman Baron, 'I am dying and you will be heir
To all the broad acres in England that William gave me for my share
When we conquered the Saxons at Hastings, and a nice little handful it is.
But before you go over to rule it I want you to understand this:

'The Saxon is not like us Normans. His manners are not so polite.
But he never means anything serious till he talks about justice and right.
When he stands like an ox in the furrow with his sullen set eyes on your own,
And grumbles "This isn't fair dealing," my son, leave the Saxon alone.

'You can horsewhip your Gascony archers, or torture your Picardy spears;
But don't try that game on the Saxon; you'll have the whole brood round
    your ears.
From the richest old Thane in the county to the poorest chained serf in the
    field,
They'll be at you and on you like hornets, and, if you are wise, you will
    yield.

'But first you must master their language, their dialect, proverbs and songs.
Don't trust any clerk to interpret when they come with the tale of their
    wrongs.
Let them know that you know what you're saying; let them feel that you
    know what to say.
Yes, even when you want to go hunting; hear 'em out if it takes you all day.

'They'll drink every hour of the daylight and poach every hour of the
    dark.
It's the sport not the rabbit they're after (we've plenty of game in the park).
Don't hang them or cut off their fingers. That's wasteful as well as
    unkind.
For a hard-bitten, South-country poacher makes the best man-at-arms
    you can find.

'Appear with your wife and the children at their weddings and funerals
    and feasts.
Be polite but not friendly to Bishops; be good to all poor parish priests.
Say "we", "us" and "ours" when you're talking, instead of "you fellows"
    and "I".
Don't ride over seeds; keep your temper; and *never you tell 'em a lie!*'

THE WISH HOUSE

First published in 1924, this short story shows Kipling writing at the top of his form. The two old Sussex women and their gossip are convincingly realised, while the supernatural tale at its heart is told with an unobtrusive attention to detail. In the two decades since Kipling first exulted over driving around the Sussex countryside, the rattle and fumes of motor transport had already become an intrusion.

The new Church Visitor had just left after a twenty minutes' call. During that time Mrs Ashcroft had used such English as an elderly, experienced and pensioned cook should, who had seen life in London. She was the readier, therefore, to slip back into easy, ancient Sussex ('t's softening to 'd's as one warmed) when the bus brought Mrs Fettley from thirty miles away for a visit that pleasant March Saturday. The two had been friends since childhood; but, of late, destiny had separated their meetings by long intervals.

Much was to be said, and many ends, loose since last time, to be ravelled up on both sides, before Mrs Fettley, with her bag of quilt-patches, took the couch beneath the window commanding the garden, and the football ground in the valley below.

'Most folk got out at Bush Tye for the match there,' she explained, 'so there weren't no one for me to cushion agin the last five mile. An' she do just-about bounce ye.'

'You've took no hurt,' said her hostess. 'You don't brittle by agein', Liz.'

Mrs Fettley chuckled and made to match a couple of patches to her liking.

'No, or I'd ha' broke twenty year back. You can't ever mind when I was so's to be called round, can ye?'

Mrs Ashcroft shook her head slowly – she never hurried – and went on stitching a sack-cloth lining into a list-bound rush tool-basket. Mrs Fettley laid out more patches in the spring light through the geraniums on the window-sill, and they were silent awhile.

'What like's this new Visitor o' yourn?' Mrs Fettley inquired with a nod towards the door. Being very short-sighted she had, on her entrance, almost bumped into the lady.

Mrs Ashcroft suspended the big packing-needle judicially on high ere she stabbed home. 'Settin' aside she don't bring much news with her yet, I dunno as I've anythin' special agin her.'

'Ourn, at Keyneslade,' said Mrs Fettley, 'she's full o' words an' pity, but she don't stay for answers. Ye can get on with your thoughts while she clacks.'

'This 'un don't clack. She's aimin' to be one o' those High Church nuns, like.'

'Ourns married, but, by what they say, she've made no great gains of it . . .'

Mrs Fettley threw up her sharp chin.

'Lord! How they dam' cherubim do shake the very bones o' the place!'

The tile-sided cottage trembled at the passage of two specially chartered forty-seat charabancs on their way to the Bush Tye match; a regular Saturday 'shopping' bus, for the county's capital, fumed behind them; while, from one of the crowded inns, a fourth car backed out to join the procession, and held up the stream of through pleasure-traffic.

'You're as free-tongued as ever, Liz,' Mrs Ashcroft observed.

'Only when I'm with you. Otherwhiles I'm Granny – three times over. I lay that basket's for one o' your gran'chiller – ain't it?'

''Tis for Arthur – my Jane's eldest.'

'But he ain't workin' nowheres, is he?'

'No. 'Tis a picnic basket.'

'You're let off light. My Willie, he's allus at me for money for them aireated wash-poles folk put up in their gardens to draw the music from Lunnon, like. An' I give it 'im – pore fool me!'

'An' he forgets to give you the promise-kiss after, don't he?' Mrs Ashcroft's heavy smile seemed to strike inwards.

'He do. No odds 'twixt boys now an' forty year back. Take all an' give naught – 'an we to put up with it! Pore fool we! Three shillin' at a time Willie'll ask me for!'

'They don't make nothin' o' money these days,' Mrs Ashcroft said.

'An' on'y last week,' the other went on, 'me daughter, she ordered a quarter-pound suet at the butchers; an' she sent it back to 'im to be chopped. She said she couldn't bother with choppin' it.'

'I lay he charged her, then.'

'I lay he did. She told me there was a whisk-drive that afternoon at the Institute, an' she couldn't bother to do the choppin'.'

'Tck!'

Mrs Ashcroft put the last firm touches to the basket lining. She had scarcely finished when her sixteen-year-old grandson, a maiden of the moment in attendance, hurried up the garden path shouting to know if the thing were ready, snatched it and made off without acknowledgement. Mrs Fettley peered at him closely.

'They're goin' picknickin' somewheres,' Mrs Ashcroft explained.

'Ah,' said the other, with narrowed eyes. 'I lay he won't show much

150

mercy to any he comes across, either. Now 'oo the dooce do he remind me of, all of a sudden?'

'They must look arter theirselves – same as we did.' Mrs Ashcroft began to set out the tea.

'No denyin' you could, Gracie,' said Mrs Fettley.

'What's in our head now?'

'Dunno . . . But it come over me, sudden-like – about dat woman from Rye – I've slipped the name – Barnsley, wadn't it?'

'Batten – Polly Batten, you're thinkin' of.'

'That's it – Polly Batten. That day she had it in for you with a hay-fork – time we was all hayin' at Smalldene – for stealin' her man.'

'But you heered me tell her she had my leave to keep him?' Mrs Aschroft's voice and smile were smoother than ever.

'I did – an' we was all looking that she'd prod the fork sprang through your breastes when you said it.'

'No-oo. She'd never go beyond bounds – Polly. She shruck too much for reel doin's.'

'Allus seems to me,' Mrs Fettley said after a pause, 'that a man 'twixt two fightin' wmen is the foolishest thing on earth. Like a dog bein' called two ways.'

'Mebbe. But what set ye off on those times, Liz?'

'That boy's fashion o' carryin' his head an' arms. I haven't rightly looked at him since he's growed. Your Jane never showed it, but – him! Why, 'tis Jim Batten and his tricks come to life again! . . . Eh?'

'Mebbe. There's some that would ha' made it out so – bein' barren-like themselves.'

'Oho! Ah well! Dearie, dearie me, now! . . . An' Jim Batten's been dead this – '

'Seven and twenty years,' Mrs Ashcroft answered briefly. 'Won't ye draw up, Liz?'

Mrs Fettley drew up to buttered toast, currant bread, stewed tea, bitter as leather, some home-preserved pears and a cold boiled pig's tail to help down the muffins. She paid all the proper compliments.

'Yes. I dunno as I've ever owed me belly much,' said Mrs Ashcroft thoughtfully. 'We only go through this world once.'

'But don't it lay heavy on ye, sometimes?' her guest suggested.

'Nurse says I'm a sight liker to die o' me indigestion than me leg.' For Mrs Ashcroft had a long-standing ulcer on her shin, which needed regular care from the Village Nurse, who boasted (or others did, for her) that she had dressed it one hundred and three times already during her term of office.

'An' you that was so able, too! It's all come on ye before your full time, like. I've watched ye goin'.' Mrs Fettley spoke with real affection.

'Somethin's bound to find ye sometime. I've me 'eart left me still,' Mrs Ashcroft returned.

'You was always big-hearted enough for three. That's somethin' to look back on at the day's eend.'

'I reckon you've your back-lookin's, too,' was Mrs Ashcroft's answer.

'You know it. But I don't think much regardin' such matters excep' when I'm along with you, Gra'. Takes two sticks to make a fire.'

Mrs Fettley stared, with jaw half-dropped, at the grocer's bright calendar on the wall. The cottage shook again to the roar of the motor traffic, and the crowded football ground below the garden roared almost as loudly; for the village was well set to its Saturday leisure.

Mrs Fettley had spoken very precisely for some time without interruption, before she wiped her eyes. 'And,' she concluded, 'they read 'is death-notice to me, out o' the paper last month. O' course it wasn't any o' my becomin' concerns – let be I 'adn't set eyes on him for so long. O' course I couldn't say nor show nothin'. Nor I've no rightful call to go to Eastbourne to see 'is grave, either. I've been schemin' to slip over there by the bus some day; but they'd ask questions at 'ome past endurance. So I 'aven't even that to stay me.'

'But you've 'ad your satisfactions?'

'Godd! Yess! Those four years 'e was workin' on the rail near us. An' the other drivers they gave him a brave funeral, too.'

'Then you've naught to cast-up about. 'Nother cup o' tea?'

The light and air had changed a little with the sun's descent, and the two elderly laides closed the kitchen door against chill. A couple of jays squealed and skirmished through the undraped apple trees in the garden. This time the word was with Mrs Ashcroft, her elbows on the tea-table, and her sick leg propped on a stool . . .

'Well I never! But what did your 'usband say to that?' Mrs Fettley asked, when the deep-toned recital halted.

''E said I might go where I pleased for all of 'im. But seein' 'e was bedrid, I said I'd tend 'im out. 'E knowed I wouldn't take no advantage of 'im in that state. 'E lasted eight or nine week. Then he was took with a seizure, like; an' laid stone-still for days. Then 'e propped 'imself up abed an' says: "You pray no man'll ever deal with you like you've dealed with some." "An' you?" I says, for you know, Liz, what a rover 'e was. "It cuts both ways," says 'e, "but I'm death-wise, an' I can see what's comin' to you." He died a-Sunday an' was buried a-Thursday . . . An' yet I'd set a heap by him – one time or – did I ever?'

'You never told me that before,' Mrs Fettley ventured.

'I'm payin' ye for what ye told me just now. Him bein' dead, I wrote up, sayin' I was free for good, to that Mrs Marshall in Lunnon – which gave me my first place as kitchen maid – Lord, how long ago! She was well pleased, for they two was both gettin' on, an' I knowed their ways. You remember, Liz, I used to go to 'em in service between whiles, for years – when we wanted money, or – or my 'usband was away – on occasion.'

"E *did* get that six months at Chichester, didn't 'e?' Mrs Fettley whispered. 'We never rightly won to the bottom of it.'

'E'd ha' got more, but the man didn't die.'

'None o' your doin' was it, Gra'?'

'No! 'Twas the woman's husband this time. An' so, my man bein' dead I went back to them Marshall's, as cook, to get me legs under a gentleman's table again, and be called with a handle to me name. That was the year you shifted to Portsmouth.'

'Cosham,' Mrs Fettley corrected. 'There was a middlin' lot o' new buildin' bein' done there. My man went first, an' got the room, an' I follered.'

'Well, then, I was a year-abouts in Lunnon, all at a breath, like, four meals a day an' livin' easy. Then, 'long towards autumn, they two went travellin', like, to France; keepin' me on, for they couldn't do without me. I put the house to rights for the caretaker, an' then I slipped down 'ere to me sister Bessie – me wages in me pockets, an' all 'ands glad to be'old of me.'

'That would be when I was at Cosham,' said Mrs Fettley.

'You know, Liz, there wasn't no cheap-dog pride to folk those days, no more than there was cinemas nor whisk drives. Man or woman 'ud lay hold o' any job that promised a shillin' to the backside of it, didn't they? I was all peaked up after Lunnon, an' I thought the fresh airs 'ud serve me. So I took on at Smalldene, obligin' with a hand at the early potato-liftin', stubbin' hens an' such-like. They'd ha' mocked me sore in my kitchen in Lunnon, to see me in men's boots, an' me petticoats all shorted.'

'Did it bring ye any good?' Mrs Fettley asked.

''Twadn't for that I went. You know, 's'well's me, that na'un happens to ye till it *'as* 'appened. Your mind don't warn ye before'and of the road ye've took, till you're at the far eend of it. We've only a backwent view of our proceedin's.'

''Oo was it?'

''Arry Mockler.' Mrs Ashcroft's face puckered to the pain of her sick leg.

Mrs Fettley gasped. ''Arry? Bert Mockler's son! An' I never guessed!'

Mrs Ashcroft nodded. 'An' I told myself – an' I beleft it – that I wanted field-work.'

'What did ye get out of it?'

'The usuals. Everythin' at first – worse than naught after. I had signs an' warning a-plenty, but I took no heed of 'em. For we was burnin' rubbish one day, just when we'd come to know 'twas with – with both of us. 'Twas early in the year for burnin', an' I said so. "No!" says he. "The sooner dat old stuff's off an' done with," 'e says, "the better." 'Is face was harder'n rocks when he spoke. Then it come over me that I'd found me master, which I 'adn't ever before. I'd allus owned 'em, like.'

'Yes! Yes! They're yourn or you're theirn,' the other sighed. 'I like the right way best.'

'I didn't. But 'Arry did . . . 'Long then it come time for me to go back to Lunnon. I couldn't. I clean couldn't! So I took an' tipped a dollop o' scaldin' water out o' the copper one Monday mornin' over me left 'and and arm. Dat stayed me where I was for another fortnight.'

'Was it worth it?' said Mrs Fettley, looking at the silvery scar on the wrinkled fore-arm.

Mrs Ashcroft nodded. 'An' after that, we two made it up 'twixt us so's 'e could come to Lunnon for a job in a liv'ry stable not far from me. 'E got it. I 'tended to that. There wadn't no talk nowhere. His own mother never suspicioned how 'twas. He just slipped up to Lunnon, an' there we abode that winter, not 'alf a mile 'tother from each.'

'Ye paid 'is fare an' all, though,' Mrs Fettley spoke convincedly.

Again Mrs Ashcroft nodded. 'Dere wadn't much I didn't do for him. 'E was me master, an' – O God, help us! – we'd laugh over it walkin' together afer dark in them paved streets, an' me corns fair wrenchin' in me boots! I'd never been like that before. Ner he! Ner he!'

Mrs Fettley clucked sympathetically.

'An' when did ye come to the eend?' she asked.

'When 'e paid it all back again, every penny. Then I knowed, but I wouldn't *suffer* meself to know. "You've been mortal kind to me," he says. "Kind!" I said. "'Twixt us?" But 'e kep' all on tellin' me 'ow kind I'd been an' 'e'd never forget it all his days. I held it from off o' me for three evenin's, because I would not believe. Then 'e talked about not bein' satisfied with 'is job in the stables, an' the men there puttin' tricks on 'im, an' all they lies which a man tells when 'e's leavin' ye. I heard 'im out, neither 'elpin' nor 'inderin'. At the last I took off a liddle brooch which he'd given me an' I says: "Dat'll do. I ain't askin' na'un." An' I turned me round an' walked off to me own sufferin's. 'E didn't make 'em worse. 'E didn't come nor write after that. 'E slipped off 'ere back 'ome to 'is mother again.'

'An' 'ow often did ye look for 'en to come back?' Mrs Fettley demanded mercilessly.

'More'n once – more'd once! Goin' over the streets we'd used, I though de very pave-stones 'ud shruck out under me feet.'

'Yes,' said Mrs Fettley. 'I dunno but dat don't 'urt as much as aught else. An' dat was all yet got?'

'No. 'Twadn't. That's the curious part, if you'll believe it, Liz.'

'I do. I lay you're further off lyin' now than in all your life, Gra'.'

'I am . . . An' I suffered, like I'd not wish my most arrantest enemies to. God's Own Name! I went through the hoop that spring! One part of it was 'eddicks which I'd never known all me days before. Think o' me with an 'eddick! But I come to be grateful for 'em. They kep' me from thinkin' . . . '

''Tis like a tooth,' Mrs Fettley commented. 'It must rage an' rugg till it tortures itself quiet on ye; an' then – then there's na'un left.'

'I got enough lef' to last me all my days on earth. It come about through our charwoman's liddle girl – Sophy Ellis was 'er name – all eyes an' elbers an' hunger. I used to give 'er vittles. Otherwhiles, I took no special notice of 'er, an' a sight less, o' course when me trouble about 'Arry was on me. But – you know how liddle maids first feel it sometimes – she come to be crazy-fond o' me, pawin' an' cuddlin' all whiles; an' I 'adn't the 'eart to beat 'er off . . . One afternoon, early in spring 'twas, 'er mother 'ad sent 'er round to scutchel up what vittles she could off of us. I was settin' by the fire, me apern over me head, half-mad with the 'eddick, when she slips in. I reckon I was middlin' short with 'er. "Lor!" she says. "Is that all? I'll take it off you in two-twos!" I told her not to lay a finger on me, for I thought she'd want to stroke my forehead; an' – I ain't that make. "I won't tech ye," she says, an' slips out again. She 'adn't been gone ten minutes 'fore me old 'eddick took off quick as bein' kicked. So I went about my work.

'Prasin'ly Sophy comes back, an' creeps into my chair quiet as a mouse. 'Er eyes was deep in 'er 'ead an' 'er face all drawed. I asked 'er what 'ad 'appened. "Nothin'," she says. "Only I've got it now." "Got what?" I says. "Your 'eddick," she says, all hoarse an' sticky-lipped. "I've took it on me." "Nonsense," I says, "it went of itself when you was out. Lay still an' I'll make ye a cup o' tea." "'Twon't do no good," she says, "Till your time's up. 'Ow long do your 'eddicks last?" "Don't talk silly," I says, "or I'll send for the Doctor." It looked to me like she might be hatchin' de measles. "Oh, Mrs Ashcroft," she says, stretchin' out 'er liddle thin arms. "I do love ye." There wasn't any holdin' agin that. I took 'er into me lap an' made much of 'er. "Is it truly gone?" she says. "Yes," I says, "an' if 'twas you took it away, I'm truly grateful." "'Twas me," she says, layin' 'er cheek to mine. "No one but me knows how." An' then she said she'd changed me 'eddick for me at a Wish 'Ouse.'

'Whatt?' Mrs Fettley spoke sharply.

'A Wish House. No! I 'adn't 'eard o' such things, either. I couldn't get it straight at first, but, puttin' all together, I made out that a Wish 'Ouse 'ad to be a house which 'ad stood unlet an' empty long enough for Some One, like, to come an' in'abit there. She said a liddle girl that she'd played with in the livery-stables where 'Arry worked 'ad told 'er so. She said the girl 'ad belonged in a caravan that laid up, o' winters, in Lunnon. Gipsy, I judge.'

'Ooh! There's no sayin' what Gippos know, but I've never 'eard of a Wish 'Ouse, an' I know – some things,' said Mrs Fettley.

'Sophy said there was a Wish 'Ouse in Wadloes Road – just a few streets off, on the way to our green-grocer's. All you 'ad to do, she said, was to ring the bell an' wish your wish through the slit o' the letterbox. I asked 'er if the fairies give it 'er? "Don't ye know," she says, "there's no fairies in a Wish 'Ouse? There's on'y a Token."'

'Goo' Lord A'mighty! Where did she come by that word?' cried Mrs Fettley; for a Token is a wraith of the dead or, worse still, of the living.

'The caravan girl 'ad told 'er, she said. Well, Liz, it troubled me to 'ear 'er, an' lyin' in me arms she must ha' felt it. "That's very kind o' you," I says, holdin' 'er tight, "to wish me 'eddick away. But why didn't ye ask somethin' nice for yourself?" "You can't do that," she says. "All you'll get at a Wish 'Ouse is leave to take someone else's trouble. I've took Ma's 'eddicks, when she's been kind to me; but this is the first time I've been able to do aught for you. Oh, Mrs Ashcroft, I do just about love you." An' she goes on all like that. Liz, I tell you my 'air e'en a'most stood on end to 'ear 'er. I asked 'er what like a Token was. "I dunno," she says, "but after you've ringed the bell, you'll 'ear it run up from the basement to the front door. Then say your wish," she says, "an' go away." "The Token don't open de door to ye, then?" I says. "Oh no," she says. "You on'y 'ear gigglin', like, be'ind the front door. Then you say you'll take the trouble off of 'oo ever 'tis you've chosen for your love; an' ye'll get it," she says. I didn't ask no more – she was too 'ot an' fevered. I made much of 'er till it come time to light de gas, an' a liddle after that 'er 'eddick – mine, I suppose – took off, an' she got down an' played with the cat.'

'Well, I never!' said Mrs Fettley. 'Did – did ye foller it up, anyway?'

'She askt me to, but I wouldn't 'ave no such dealin's with a child.'

'What did ye do, then?'

'Sat in me own room 'stid o' the kitchen when me 'eddicks come on. But it lay at de back o' me mind.'

''Twould. Did she tell ye more, ever?'

'No. Besides what the Gippo girl 'ad told 'er, she knew naught, 'cept that the charm worked. An', next after that – in May 'twas – I suffered the summer out in Lunnon. 'Twas hot an' windy for weeks, an' the streets stinkin' o' dried 'orse dung blowin' from side to side an' lyin' level with the kerb. We don't get that nowadays. I 'ad my 'ol'day just before hoppin' an' come down 'ere to stay with Bessie again. She noticed I'd lost flesh, an' was all poochy under the eyes.'

'Did ye see 'Arry?'

Mrs Ashcroft nodded. 'The fourth – no, the fifth day. Wednesday 'twas. I knowed 'e was workin' at Smalldene again. I asked 'is mother in the street, bold as brass. She 'adn't room to say much, for Bessie – you know 'er tongue – was talkin' full-clack. But that Wednesday I was walkin' with one o' Bessie's chillern hangin' on me skirts, at de back o' Chanter's Tot. Prasin'ly I felt 'e was be'ind me on the footpath, an' I knowed by 'is tread 'e'd changed 'is nature. I slowed, an' I heard 'im slow. Then I fussed a piece with the child, to force him past me, like. So 'e 'ad to come past. 'E just says "Good evenin'," and goes on, tryin' to pull 'isself together.'

'Drunk, was he?' Mrs Fettley asked.

'Never! S'runk an' wizen; 'is clothes 'angin' on 'im like bags, an' the back of 'is neck whiter'n chalk. 'Twas all I could do not to oppen my arms an' cry after him. But I swallered me spittle till I was back 'ome again an' the chillern abed. Then I says to Bessie, after supper, "What in de world's come to 'Arry Mockler?" Bessie told me 'e'd been a-Hospital for two months, 'long of' cuttin 'is foot wid a spade, muckin' out the old pond at Smalldene. There was poison in de dirt, an' it rooshed up 'is leg, like, an' come out all over him. 'E 'adn't been back to 'is job – carterin' at Smalldene – more'n a fortnight. She told me the Doctor said he'd go off, likely, with the November frostes; an' 'is mother 'ad told 'er that 'e didn't rightly eat nor sleep, an' sweated 'imself into pools, no odds 'ow chill 'e lay. An' spit terrible o' mornin's. "Dearie me," I says. "But mebbe hoppin' 'll set 'im right again," an' I licked me thread-point an' I fetched me needle's eye up to it an' threads me needle under de lamp steady as rocks. An' dat night (me bed was in de wash-house) I cried an' I cried. An' you know, Liz – for you've been with me in my throes – it takes summat to make me cry.'

'Yes; but chile-bearin' is on'y just pain,' said Mrs Fettley.

'I come round by cock-crow, an' dabbed cold tea on me eyes to take away the signs. Long towards nex' evenin' – I was settin' out to lay some flowers on me 'usband's grave, for the look 'o the thing – I met 'Arry over against where the War Memorial is now. 'E was comin' back from 'is 'orses, so 'e couldn't not see me. I looked 'im all over, an' "'Arry," I says twix' me teeth, 'come back an' rest-up in Lunnon." "I won't take it," he says, "for I can give ye naught." "I don't ask it," I says. "By God's Own Name, I don't ask na'un! On'y come up an' see a Lunnon doctor." "'E lifts 'is two 'eavy eyes at me: "'Tis past that, Gra'," 'e says. "I've but a few months left." "'Arry!" I says. "My man!' I says. I couldn't say no more. 'Twas all up in me throat. "Thank ye kindly Gra'," 'e says (but 'e never says "my woman"), an' 'e went on up-street an' 'is mother – Oh, damn 'er! – she was watchin' for 'im, an' she shut de door be'ind 'im.'

Mrs Fettley stretched an arm across the table and made to finger Mrs Ashcroft's sleeve at the wrist, but the other moved it out of reach.

'So I went on to the churchyard with my flowers, an' I remembered my 'usband's warnin' that night he spoke. 'E was death-wise, an' it 'ad 'appened as 'e said. But as I was settin' down de jam-pot on the grave-mound, it come over me there was one thing I could do for 'Arry. Doctor or no Doctor, I thought I'd make a trial of it. So I did. Nex' mornin', a bill came down from our Lunnon greengrocer. Mrs Marshall, she'd lef' me petty cash for suchlike – o' course – but I tole Bess 'twas for me to come an' open the 'ouse. So I went up, afternoon train.'

'An' – but I know you 'adn't – 'adn't you no fear?'

'What for? There was nothin' front o' me but my own shame an' God's croolty. I couldn't ever get 'Arry – 'ow could I? I knowed it must go on burnin' till it burned me out.'

'Aie!' said Mrs Fettley, reaching for the wrist again, and this time Mrs Ashcroft permitted it.

'Yit t'was a comfort to know I could this for 'im. So I went an' I paid the greengrocer's bills, an' put 'is receipt in me handbag, an' then I stepped round to Mrs Ellis – our char – an' got the 'ouse-keys an' opened the 'ouse. First I made me bed to come back to (God's Own Name! me bed to lie upon!) Nex' I made me a cup o' tea an' sat down in the kitchen thinkin', till long towards dusk. Terrible close, 'twas. Then I dressed me an' went out with the receipt in me 'andbag, feignin' to study it for an address, like. Fourteen Wadloes Road was the place – a liddle basement-kitchen 'ouse, in a row of twenty-thirty such, an' tiddy strips o' walled garden in front – the paint off the front door, an' na'un done to na'un since ever so long. There wasn't 'ardly no one in the streets 'cept the cats. 'Twas 'ot, too! I turned into the gate bold as brass; up de steps I went an' I ringed the front-door bell. She pealed loud, like it do in an empty house. When she'd all ceased I 'eard a cheer, like, pushed back on de floor o' the kitchen. Then I 'eard feet on de kitchen stairs, like it might ha' been a heavy woman in slippers. They come up to de stair-head, acrost the hall – I 'eard the bare boards creak under 'em – an' at de front door dey stopped. I stooped me to the letter-box slit, an' I says: "Let me take everythin' bad that's in store for my man, 'Arry Mockford, for love's sake." Then, whatever it was 'tother side de door let its breath out, like, as if it 'ad been holdin' it for to 'ear better.'

'Nothin' was said to ye?' Mrs Fettley demanded.

'Na'un. She just breathed out – a sort of A-ah, like. Then the steps went back an' downstairs to the kitchen – all draggy – an' I heard the cheer drawed up again.'

'An' you abode on de doorstep, throughout all, Gra'?'

Mrs Ashcroft nodded.

'Then I went away, an' a man passin' says to me: "Didn't you know that house was empty?" "No," I says. "I must ha' been give the wrong number." An' I went back to our 'ouse, an' I went to bed; for I was fair flogged out. 'Twas too 'ot to sleep more'n snatches, so I walked me about, lyin' down betweens, till crack o' dawn. Then I went to the kitchen to make me a cup o' tea, an' I hitted meself just above the ankle on an old roastin'-jack o' mine that Mrs Ellis had moved out from the corner, her last cleanin'. An' so – nex' after that – I waited till the Marshalls come back o' their holiday.'

'Alone there? I'd ha' thought you'd 'ad enough of empty houses,' said Mrs Fettley, horrified.

'Oh, Mrs Ellis an' Sophy was runnin' in an' out soon's I was back, an' 'twixt us we cleaned de house again top-to-bottom. There's allus a hand's turn more to do in every house. An' that's 'ow 'twas with me that autumn an' winter, in Lunnon.'

'Then na'un hap – overtook ye for your doin's?'

Mrs Ashcroft smiled. 'No. Not then. 'Long in November I sent Bessie ten shillin's.'

'You was allus free-'anded,' Mrs Fettley interrupted.

'An' I got what I paid for, with the rest o' the news. She said the hoppin' 'ad set 'im up wonderful. 'E'd 'ad six weeks of it, and now 'e was back again carterin' at Smalldene. No odds to me 'ow it 'appened – 'slong's it 'ad. But I dunno as my ten shillin's eased me much. 'Arry bein' dead, like, 'e'd ha' been mine till Judgement. 'Arry bein' alive, 'e'd like as not pick up with some woman middlin' quick. I raged over that. Come spring, I 'ad somethin' else to rage for. I'd growed a nasty little weepin' boil, like, on me shin, just above the boot-top, that wouldn't heal no shape.

'It made me sick to look at it, for I'm clean-fleshed by nature. Chop me all over with a spade, an' I'd heal like turf. Then Mrs Marshall she set 'er own doctor at me. 'E said I ought to ha' come to him at first go-off, 'stead o' drawin' all manner o' dyed stockin's over it for months. 'E said I'd stood up too much for me work, for it was settin' very close atop of a big swelled vein, like, behither the small o' me ankle. "Slow come, slow go," 'e says. "Lay your leg up on high an' rest it," he says, "an' 'twill ease off. Don't let it close up too soon. You've got a very fine leg, Mrs Ashcroft," 'e says. An' 'e put wet dressin's on it.'

''E done right.' Mrs Fettley spoke firmly. 'Wet dressin's to wet wounds. They draw de humours, same's a lamp-wick draws de oil.'

'That's true. An' Mrs Marshall was allus at me to make me set down more, an' dat night healed it up. An' then after a while they packed me off down to Bessie's to finish the cure; for I ain't the sort to sit down when I ought to stand up. You was back in the village then, Liz.'

'I was. I was, but – never did I guess!'

'I didn't desire ye to.' Mrs Ashcroft smiled. 'I saw 'Arry once or twice in de street, wonnerful fleshed up an' restored back. Then, one day I didn't see 'im, an' 'is mother told me one of 'is 'orses 'ad lashed out an' caught 'im on the 'ip. So 'e wa abed an' middlin' painful. An' Bessie, she says to his mother, 'twas a pity 'Arry 'adn't a woman of 'is own to take the nursin' off 'er. And the old lady was mad! She told us that 'Arry 'ad never looked after any woman in 'is born days, an' as long as she was atop the mowlds, she'd contrive for 'im till 'er two 'ands cropped off. So I knowed she'd to watch-dog for me, 'thout askin' for bones.'

Mrs Fettley rocked with small laughter.

'That day,' Mrs Ashcroft went on, 'I'd stood on me feet nigh all the time, watchin' the doctor go in an' out; for they thought it might be 'is ribs, too. That made my boil break again, issuin' and weepin'. But it turned out 'twadn't ribs at all, an' 'Arry 'ad a good night. When I heard that, nex' mornin', I says to meself, "I won't lay two an' two together yit. I'll keep me leg down a week an' see what comes of it." It didn't hurt me that day, to speak of – seemed more to draw the strength out o' me like – an' 'Arry 'ad another good night. That made me persevere; but I didn't dare lay two an' two together till the week-end, an' then 'Arry come forth e'en a'most 'imself again – na'un hurt outside ner in of him. I nigh fell on me knees in de wash-house when Bessie was up-street. "I've got ye now, my man," I says. "You'll take your good from me 'thougt known' it till my life's end. O God, send me long to live for 'Arry's sake!" I says. An' I dunno that didn't still me ragin's.'

'For good?' Mrs Fettley asked.

'They come back, plenty times, but, let be how 'twould, I knowed I was doin' for 'im. I knowed it. I took an' worked me pains on an' off, like regulatin' my own rage, till I learned to 'ave 'em at my commandments. An' that was funny, too. There was times, Liz, when my trouble 'ud all s'rink an' dry up, like. First, I used to try an' fetch it on again; bein' fearful to leave 'Arry alone too long for anythin' to lay 'old of. Prasin'ly I come to see that was a sign he'd do all right awhile, an' so I saved myself.'

''Ow long for?' Mrs Fettley asked, with deepest interest.

'I've gone de better part of a year once or twice with na'un more to show than the liddle weepin' core of it, like. All s'rinked up an' dried off.

Then he'd inflame up – for a warnin' – an' I'd suffer it. When I couldn't no more – an' I 'ad to keep on goin' with my Lunnon work – I'd lay me leg high on a cheer till it eased. Not too quick. I knowed by the feel of it, those times dat 'Arry was in need. Then I'd send another five shillin's to Bess, or somethin' for the chillern, to find out if, mebbe, 'e'd took any hurt through my neglects. 'Twas so! Year in, year out, I worked it dat way, Liz, an' 'e got 'is good from me 'thout knowin' – for years and years.'

'But what did you get out of it, Gra'?' Mrs Fettley almost wailed. 'Did ye see 'im reg'lar?'

'Times – when I was 'ere on me 'ol'days. An' more, now that I'm 'ere for good. But 'e's never looked at me, ner any other woman 'cept 'is mother. 'Ow I used to watch an' listen! So did she.'

'Years an' years!' Mrs Fettley repeated. 'An' where's 'e workin' at now?'

'Oh, 'e's give up carterin' quite a while. He's workin' for one o' them big tractorisin' firms – plowin' sometimes, an' sometimes off with lorries – fur as Wales, I've 'eard. He comes 'ome to 'is mother 'tween whiles; but I don't set eyes on him now fer weeks on end. No odds! 'Is job keeps 'im from continuin' in one stay anywheres.'

'But – just for de sake o' sayin' somethin' – s'pose 'Arry did get married?' said Mrs Fettley.

Mrs Ashcroft drew her breath sharply between her still even and natural teeth. 'Dat ain't been required of me,' she answered. 'I reckon my pains 'ull be counted agin that. Don't you, Liz?'

'It ought to be, dearie. It ought to be.'

'It do 'urt sometimes. You shall see it when Nurse comes. She thinks I don't know it's turned.'

Mrs Fettley understood. Human nature seldom walks up to the word 'cancer'.

'Be ye certain sure, Gra'?' she asked.

'I was sure of it when old Mr Marshall 'ad me up to 'is study an' spoke a long piece about my faithful service. I've obliged 'em on an' off for a goodish time, but not enough for a pension. But they give me a weekly 'lowance for life. I knew what that sinnified – as long as three years ago.'

'Dat don't prove it Gra'.'

'To give fifteen bob a week to a woman 'oo'd live twenty year in the course o' nature? It do!'

'You're mistook! You're mistook!' Mrs Fettley insisted.

'Liz, there's no mistakin' when the edges are all heaped up, like – same as a collar. You'll see it. An' I laid out Dora Wickwood, too. She 'ad it under the arm-pit, like.'

Mrs Fettley considered awhile, and bowed her head in finality.

"Ow long d'you reckon 'twill allow ye, countin' from now, dearie?'

'Slow come, slow go. But if I don't set eyes on ye 'fore next hoppin', this'll be goodbye, Liz.'

'Dunno as I'll be able to manage by then – not 'thout I have a liddle dog to lead me. For de chillern, dey won't be troubled, an' – O Gra'! – I'm blindin' up – I'm blindin' up!'

'Oh, dat was why you didn't more'n finger with our quilt patches all this while! I was wonderin' . . . But the pain do count, don't ye think, Liz? The pain do count to keep 'Arry – where I want 'im. Say it can't be wasted, like.'

'I'm sure of it – sure of it, dearie. You'll 'ave your reward.'

'I don't want no more'n this – if de pain is taken into de reckonin'.'

"Twill be – 'twill be, Gra'.'

There was a knock on the door.

'That's Nurse. She's before 'er time,' said Mrs Ashcroft. 'Open to 'er.'

The young lady entered briskly, all the bottles in her bag clicking. 'Evenin', Mrs Ashcroft,' she began. 'I've come raound a little earlier than usual because of the Institute dance to-na-ite. You won't ma-ind, will you?'

'Oh, no. Me dancin' days are over.' Mrs Ashcroft was the self-contained domestic at once. 'My old friend, Mrs Fettley 'ere, has been settin' talkin' with me a while.'

'I hope she 'asn't been fatiguing you?' said the Nurse a little frostily.

'Quite the contrary. It 'as been a pleasure. Only – only – just at the end I felt a bit – a bit flogged out like.'

'Yes, yes.' The Nurse was on her knees already, with the washes to hand. 'When the old ladies get together they talk a deal too much, I've noticed.'

'Mebbe we do,' said Mrs Fettley, rising. 'So now I'll make myself scarce.'

'Look at it first, though,' said Mrs Ashcroft feebly. 'I'd like ye to look at it.'

Mrs Fettley looked, and shivered. Then she leaned over and kissed Mrs Ashcroft once on the waxy yellow forehead, and again on the faded grey eyes.

'It do count, don't it – de pain?' The lips that still kept trace of their original moulding hardly more than breathed the words.

Mrs Fettley kissed them and moved towards the door.

'Very Many People'

On the Downs, in the Weald, on the Marshes,
  I heard the Old Gods say:
'Here come Very Many People:
  We must go away.

'They take our land to delight in,
  But their delight destroys.
They flay the turf from the sheep-walk.
  They load the Denes with noise.

'They burn coal in the woodland.
  They seize the oast and the mill.
They camp beside Our dew-ponds.
  They mar the clean-flanked hill.

'They string a clamorous Magic
  To fence their souls from thought,
'Till Our deep-breathed Oaks are silent,
  And Our muttering Downs tell nought.

'They comfort themselves with neighbours.
  They cannot bide alone.
It shall be best for their doings
  When We Old Gods are gone.'

Farewell to the Downs and the Marshes,
  And the Weald and the Forest known
Before there were Very Many People,
  And the Old Gods had gone!

PLACES TO VISIT

Bateman's, Burwash
OS map reference TQ 671238
National Trust
Telephone 01435 882302
Kipling's house was left to the National Trust by his widow, and most of the rooms are much as he left them, among  them the atmospheric study complete with his writing materials and other favourite objects on the desk. One of the author's Rolls-Royces can be seen in the garage. The grounds run down to the River Dudwell with its watermill. There is a shop and a tea-room.

The Grange Museum, Rottingdean
OS map reference TQ 369025
Entrance free
Telephone 01273 301004
Originally the vicarage, The Grange lies close to Kipling's former home, The Elms, and houses both a library and a  museum. The latter includes a room dedicated to the author, with a good deal of memorabilia and an accurate reconstruction of his former study.